NEXT STATION 1

WORKBOOK

Amanda Cant / Mary Charrington

macmillan education

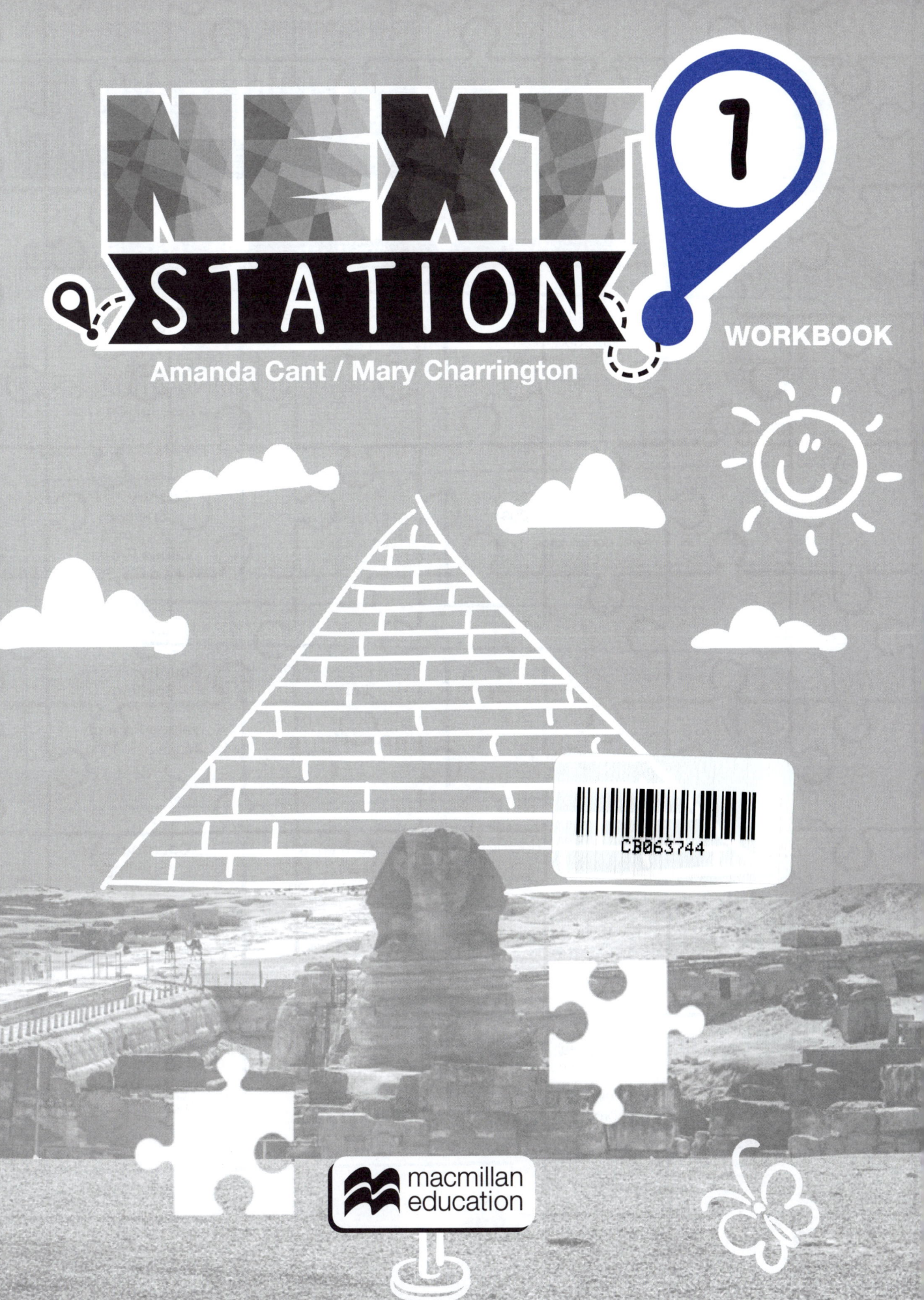

CONTENTS

	VOCABULARY	GRAMMAR	FEATURES
 **UNIT 1** PAGES 4-10	hello, hi, goodbye, bye mom, dad, brother, sister, grandma, grandpa	What's your name? My name's … This is my …	**Country:** USA **Spelling:** a, o, h, t **Values Project:** Make Friendship Tokens
 **UNIT 2** PAGES 11-19	panda, tiger, fish, monkey, elephant, octopus desk, pencil case, board, door, window, clock	What is it? It's a / an … Is it a / an …? Yes, it is. / No, it isn't.	**Country:** China **Spelling:** u, c, m, d **Values Project:** Make a Car Sticker
 **UNIT 3** PAGES 20-26	one, two, three, four, five, six, seven, eight, nine, ten pen, pencil, eraser, book, ruler, backpack	How old are you? I'm … one book / two books one pen / three pens	**Country:** Russia **Spelling:** e, i, p, b **Values Project:** Make a Sharing Display
 **UNIT 4** PAGES 27-35	teacher, actor, doctor, farmer, cook, artist singer, dancer, taekwondo instructor, engineer, inventor, soccer player	His / Her name's … He's / She's a / an … He / She isn't a / an … Is he / she a / an …? Yes, he / she is. / No, he / she isn't.	**Country:** Spain **Spelling:** s, y, f, x **Values Project:** Make *I'm Sorry* Cards
 **UNIT 5** PAGES 36-42	doll, computer game, teddy bear, robot, bike, kite red, yellow, blue, green, pink, brown, gray, white, black, orange	What are they? They're … Are they (color)? Yes, they are. / No, they aren't.	**Country:** Egypt **Spelling:** w, k, g, q, r **Values Project:** Make an Invitation

	VOCABULARY	GRAMMAR	FEATURES
 **PAGES 43-51**	cat, dog, rabbit, turtle, bird, horse snake, spider, iguana, mouse, frog, hamster	I have a / an … I don't have a / an … Do you have a / an …? Yes, I do. / No, I don't.	**Country:** Mexico **Spelling:** l, j, z, v, n **Values Project:** Make a Pet Chart
 **PAGES 52-58**	hair, eyes, ears, nose, mouth, teeth legs, arms, feet, hands, fingers, toes	He / She / It has … Does he / she / it have …? Yes, he / she / it does. / No, he / she / it doesn't.	**Country:** India **Spelling:** ll, zz **Values Project:** Make a *Be Clean* Chart
 **PAGES 59-67**	pool, park, mall, stadium, school, zoo tree, river, beach, mountain, flower, lake	There's a / an … There isn't a / an … Is there a …? Yes, there is. / No, there isn't.	**Country:** UK **Spelling:** ss, ff **Values Project:** Make a Litter Poster
 **PAGES 68-74**	apple, banana, pear, orange, pineapple, watermelon eleven, twelve, thirteen, fourteen, fifteen, sixteen, seventeen, eighteen, nineteen, twenty	There's one … There are (number) … s. How many … s are there? There are (number) … s.	**Country:** Brazil **Spelling:** ch, sh **Values Project:** Make a Lost Property Box
 **PAGES 75-83**	table, closet, TV, bed, sofa, chair bedroom, bathroom, living room, kitchen, garage, yard	The … is in / on / under the … Where's the … ? It's in / on / under the …. Where are the … s? They're in / on / under the …	**Country:** Japan **Spelling:** nk, ng **Values Project:** Make a Pencil Box

PAGES D1–D10 MY DICTIONARY   PAGE 95 PROGRESS RECORD

UNIT 1 — Lesson 1

VOCABULARY

1 Look and circle.

1. Hello. / (Goodbye.)

2. Hello. / Goodbye.

3. Hi. / Bye.

4. Hi. / Bye.

2 Draw a picture of yourself. Then write your name.

Hi, I'm Beakie.

Hello, I'm _____.

DICTIONARY page D1

Lesson 2 GRAMMAR

1 Look and connect.

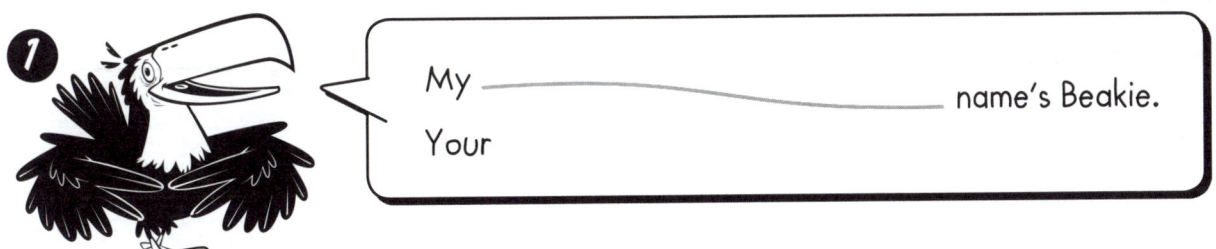

2 Connect to make a question and answer.

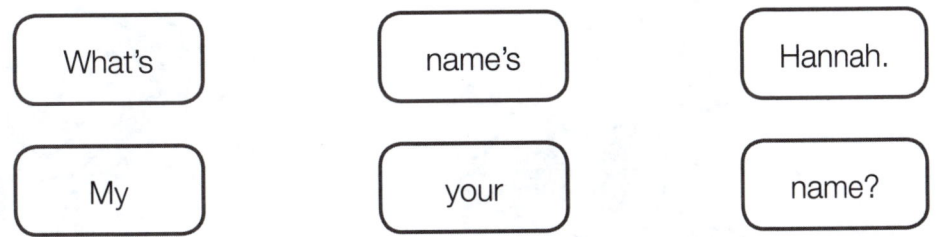

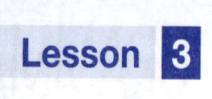

Lesson 3

SPELLING

1 Read. Then underline <u>a</u>, <u>o</u>, <u>h</u>, and <u>t</u>.

2 Write *a*, *o*, *h*, or *t*.

Lesson 4

VALUES PROJECT

MAKE FRIENDSHIP TOKENS
Be friendly!

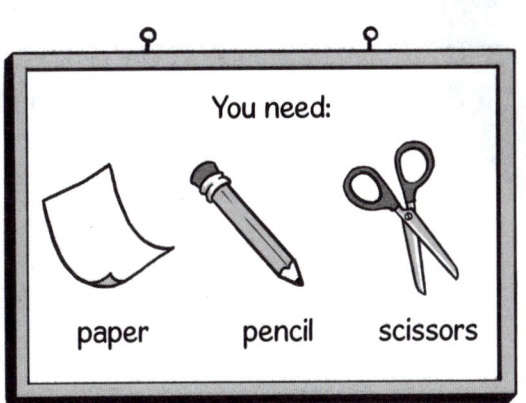

You need: paper, pencil, scissors

Draw 6 circles.

Draw smiley faces.

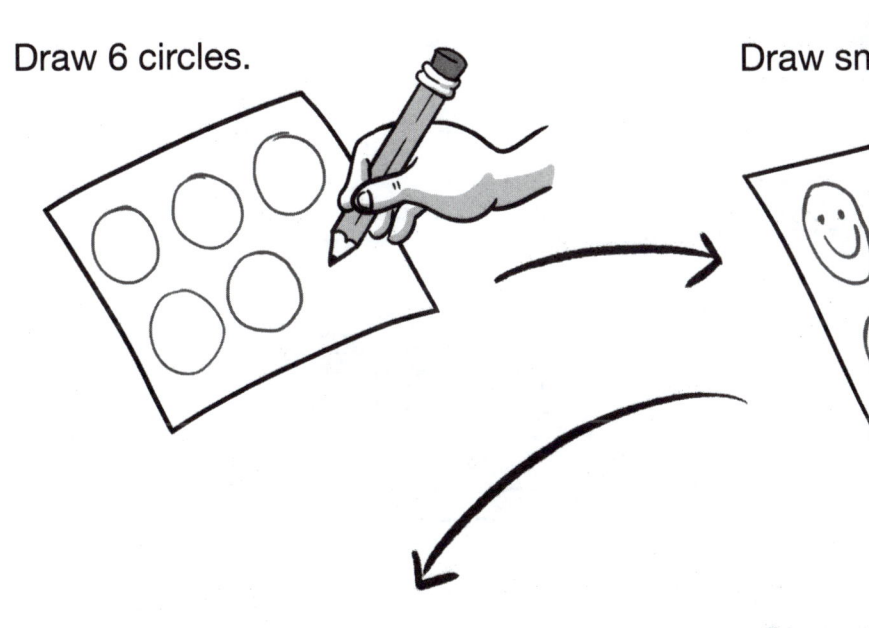

Cut.

Give your tokens to your classmates.

Hi, I'm Amy. Let's be friends!

About Me
Who are your friends at school?

Lesson 5

VOCABULARY

1 Match the words and pictures.

1 grandpa
2 sister
3 mom
4 brother
5 dad
6 grandma

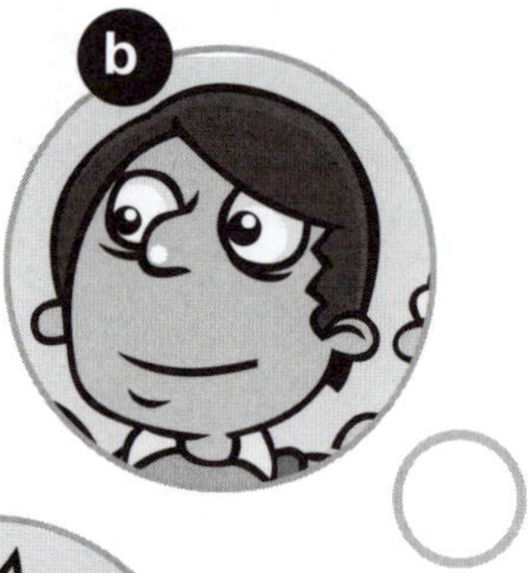

1

2 Listen and circle.

1 Hello, Mom. / Grandma.
I love you.
Hello, Jim.
I love you, too.

2 Hello, Mom. / Dad.
I love you.
Hello, Jim.
I love you, too.

3 Hello, Grandma. / Grandpa.
I love you.
Hello, Jim.
I love you, too.

4 Hello, Dad. / Grandpa.
I love you.
Hello, Jim.
I love you, too.

Lesson 6

GRAMMAR

1 Number the words in the correct order.

my ○　　This ①　　mom. ○　　is ○

2 Look and check (✓).

a This is my dad. ○
b This is my mom. ✓

a This is my dad. ○
b This is my grandpa. ○

a This is my brother. ○
b This is my sister. ○

9

Lesson 7 and 8

LET'S VISIT THE USA

1 Connect the pictures and sentences.

a This is a hamburger.

b Hi! I'm a cowboy.

c My name's Helen.

2 Connect the dots. Then read and circle.

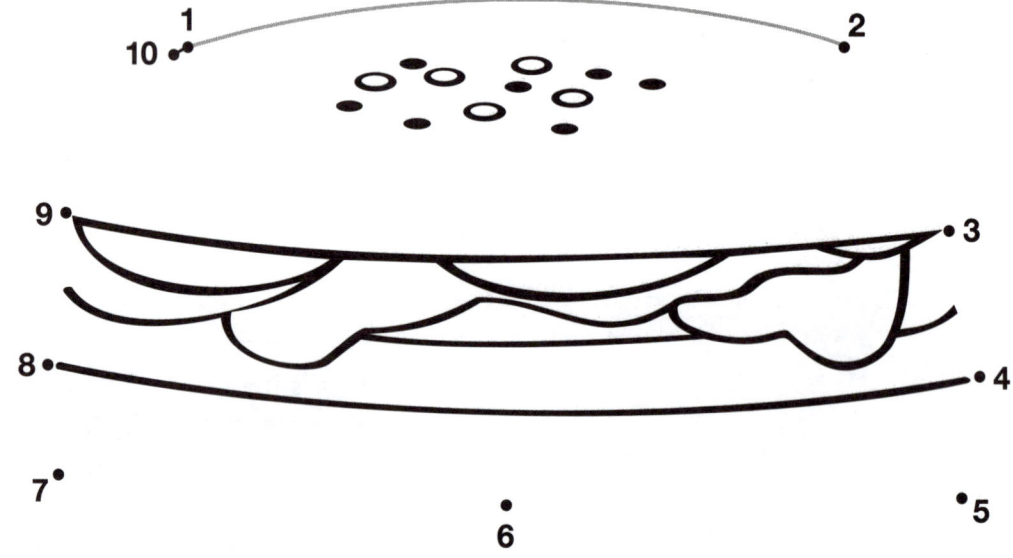

This is a cowboy / hamburger.

Lesson 1

VOCABULARY

1 Connect the pictures and words.

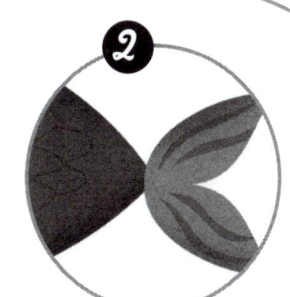

a elephant

b octopus

c fish

d monkey

e panda

f tiger

2 Circle the words. Then draw the missing animal from Activity 1.

DICTIONARY
page D2

Lesson 2

GRAMMAR

1 Circle *a* or *an*.

1. It's (a) / an panda.

2. It's a / an octopus.

3. It's a / an elephant.

4. It's a / an tiger.

2 Read. Then find and color the animals in Activity 1.

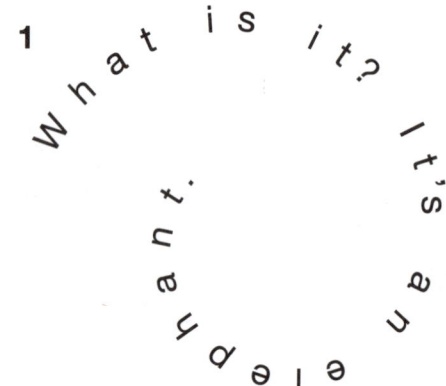

1. What is it? It's an elephant.

2. What is it? It's a tiger.

Lesson 3 · SPELLING ·

1 Read. Then underline *u*, *c*, *m*, and *d*.

This is Sandy and her mom.   This is a hut.   And this is a cat.

2 Write *u*, *c*, *m*, or *d*.

1 This is San___y.

2 This is her ___o___.

3 This is a h___t.

4 This is a ___at.

13

Lesson 4

MAKE A CAR STICKER

Be careful!

· VALUES PROJECT ·

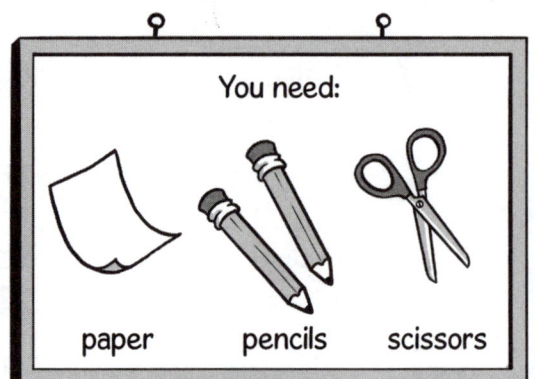

You need:

paper   pencils   scissors

Draw and cut.

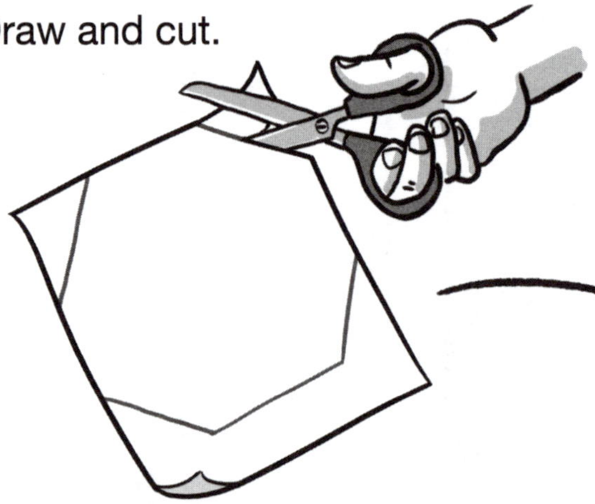

Write: **Be careful!**

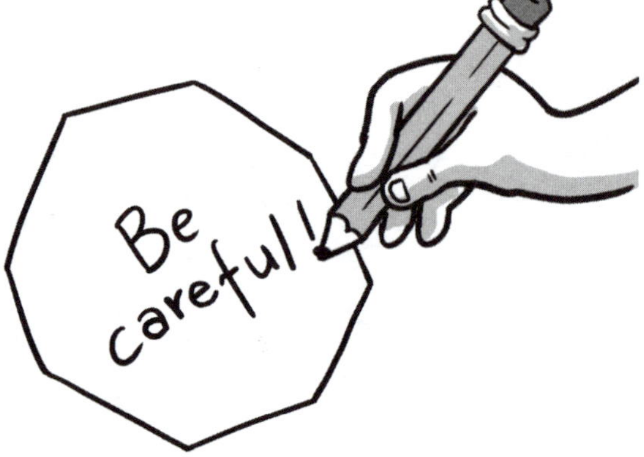

Decorate.

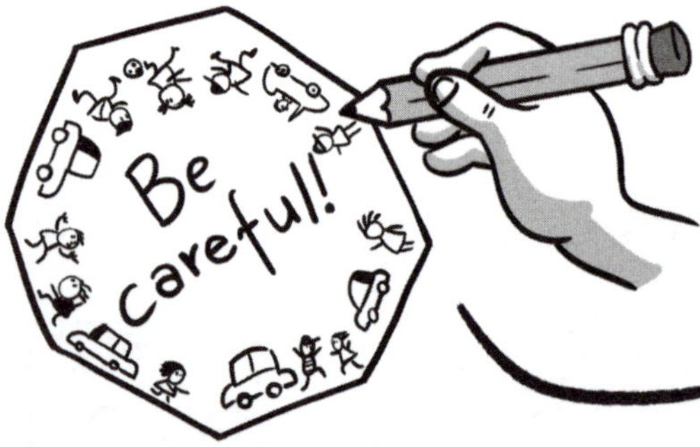

Put the sticker in your car.

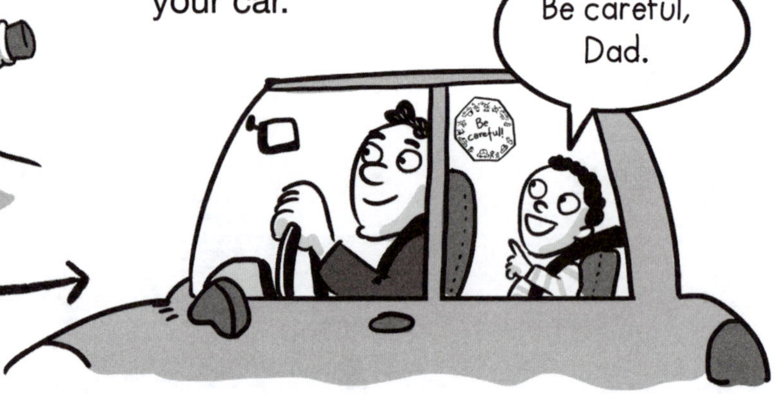

Be careful, Dad.

About Me
How do you cross the street safely?

14

Lesson 5 ·VOCABULARY·

1 Find and circle the words.

❶
ro d o o r od

❷
c l pencil ne secasesc

❸
s k e d e s k e

❹
w n window d w

❺
k c l o c k o k

❻
r d a b o a r d r

TRACK 20

2 Listen, read, and connect in the correct order.

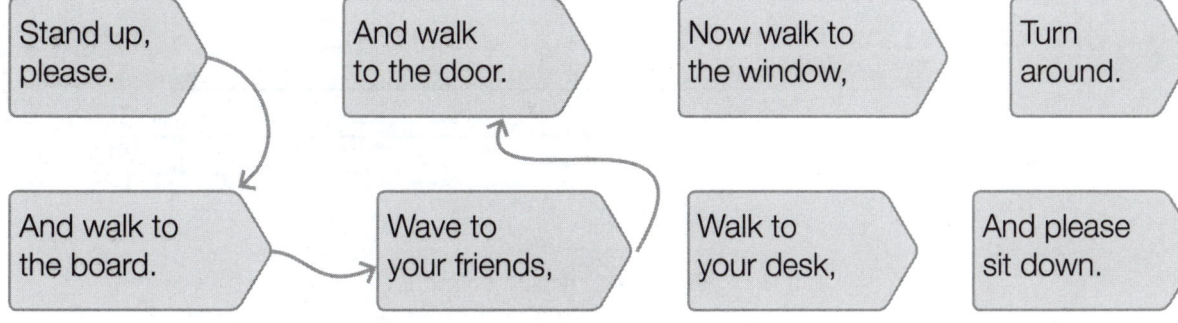

DICTIONARY
page D2

15

Lesson 6

· GRAMMAR ·

1 Connect. Then look and check (✓).

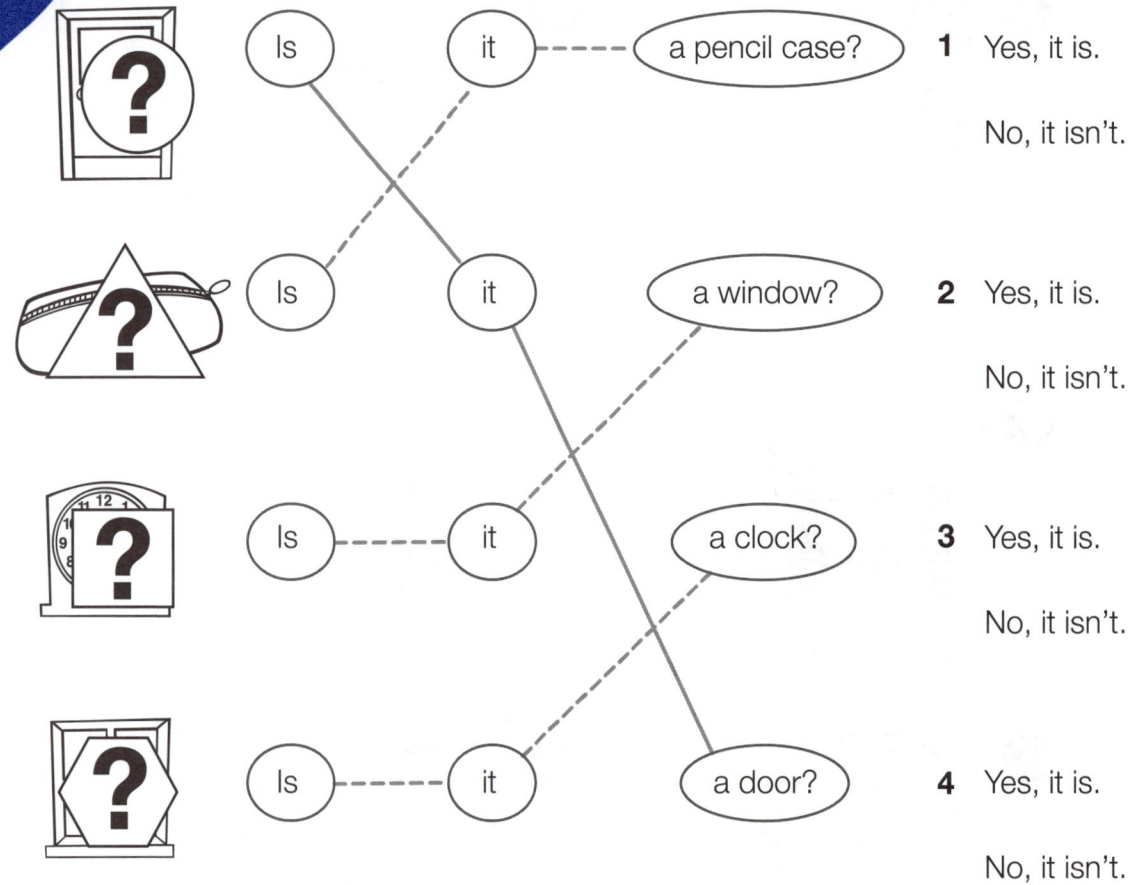

2 Connect the dots. Then read and circle.

Is it a board? Yes, it is. / No, it isn't.

Lessons 7 and 8

LET'S VISIT CHINA

1 Match the pictures and words. Then circle the animals from China.

a panda   **b** elephant   **c** dragon (1)   **d** tiger

2 Number the sentences in the correct order.

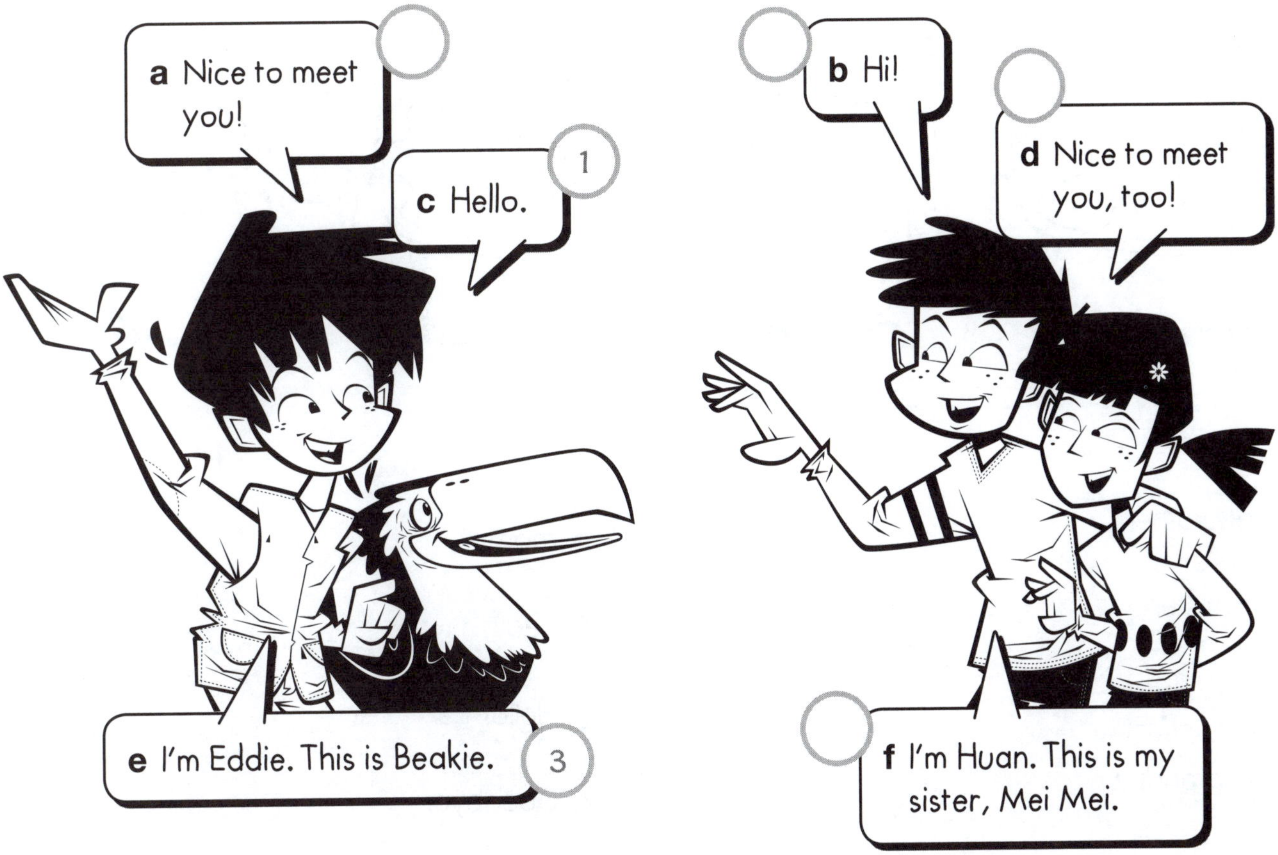

a Nice to meet you!

c Hello. (1)

e I'm Eddie. This is Beakie. (3)

b Hi!

d Nice to meet you, too!

f I'm Huan. This is my sister, Mei Mei.

17

PLAY TIME

Look at the pictures and check (✓).

	1	2
a brother	○	✓
b sister	○	○
c grandma	○	○
d grandpa	○	○

	1	2
e mom	○	○
f dad	○	○
g Hello!	○	○
h Goodbye!	○	○

PLAY TIME

Look and check (✓) the things in the picture.

elephant ✓	dragon ○	fish ○	board ○
tiger ○	octopus ○	monkey ○	cat ○
panda ○	dog ○	clock ○	hut ○

19

Lesson 1

VOCABULARY

1 Cross out (✗) the one that's different.

a | 2 | ~~three~~ | two
b | seven | **five** | 5
c | three | nine | 3
d | eight | 8 | 2
e | 3 | 10 | ten
f | six | one | 6
g | 7 | four | 4
h | 1 | one | 3
i | seven | 7 | six
j | nine | eight | 9

2 Write numbers to make ten.

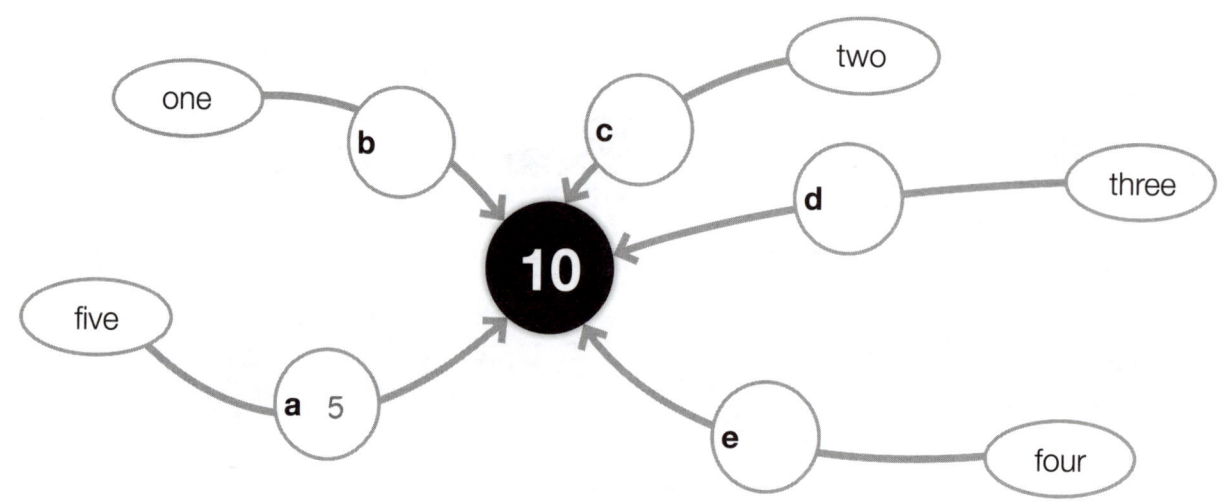

DICTIONARY page D3

Lesson 2

GRAMMAR

1 Look and circle.

I'm seven. / I'm five.

I'm ten. / I'm six.

I'm two. / I'm nine.

I'm three. / I'm four.

2 Draw a picture of yourself and the correct number of candles on the cake. Then write.

I'm _____.

I'm three. How old are you?

Lesson 3

· SPELLING ·

1 Read. Then underline <u>e</u>, <u>i</u>, <u>p</u>, and <u>b</u>.

This is my brother. He's six. And this is a pencil case.

This is a desk and this is my grandpa.

2 Write e, i, p, or b.

1 Th__s __s my __roth__r.

2 Th__s __s a __ __nc__l case.

3 Th__s __s my grand__a.

Lesson 4

MAKE A SHARING DISPLAY

It's good to share!

VALUES PROJECT

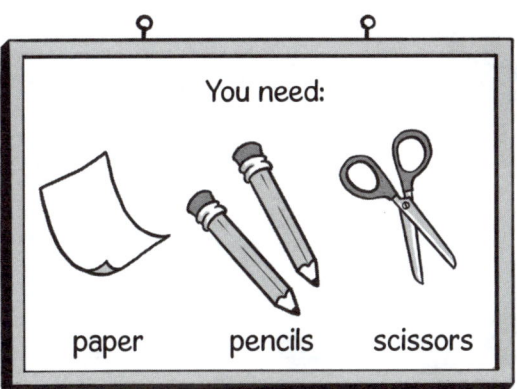

Draw around your hand.

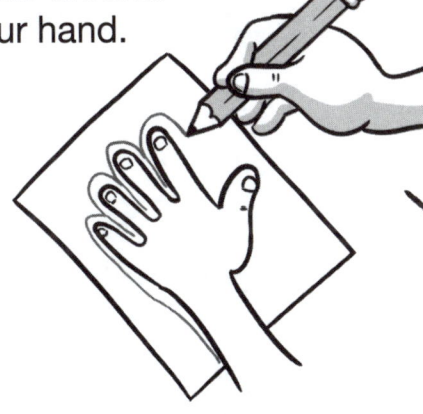

Cut.

Draw pictures of two things you can share.

Make a group display.

About Me
What do you share with family and friends?

UNIT 3 — Lesson 5 — · VOCABULARY ·

1 Match the words and pictures.

1 pencil	3 backpack	5 eraser
2 pen	4 ruler	6 book

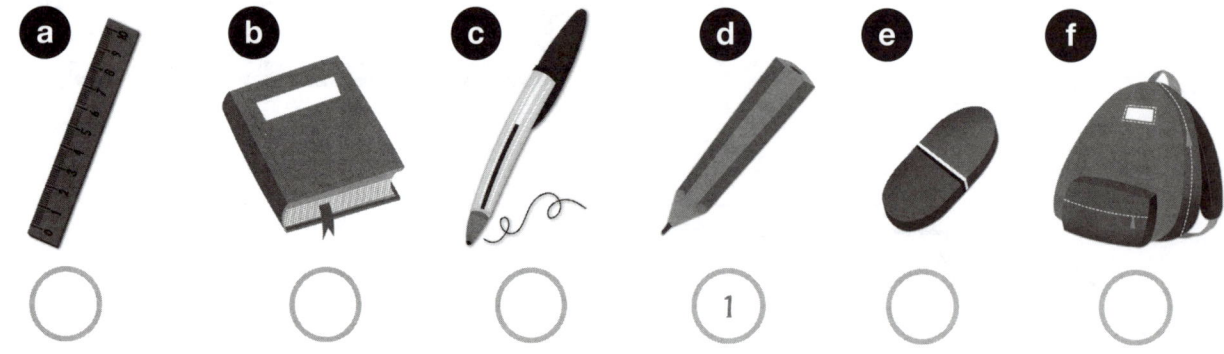

a ○   b ○   c ○   d (1)   e ○   f ○

TRACK 30

2 Listen, read, and draw the objects in the correct order.

Pick up a **pencil**,
Pick up a **pen**,
Pick up a **book**,
And count to 10!

1, 2, 3, 4, 5, 6,
7, 8, 9, 10!

Pick up a **backpack**,
Pick up a **pen**,
Pick up an **eraser**,
And count to 10!

1, 2, 3, 4, 5, 6,
7, 8, 9, 10!

| 1 | 2 | 3 |
| 4 | 5 | 6 |

DICTIONARY page D3

Lesson 6

· GRAMMAR ·

1 Look and circle. Then connect.

1 three eraser / (erasers)   5
2 one backpack / backpacks   3
3 five pencil / pencils   1

2 Follow the path. Then count and write.

1 _4_ pen_s_   2 ___ pencil___   3 ___ backpack___   4 ___ ruler___

Lessons **7 and 8**

LET'S VISIT RUSSIA

1 Count and write the number. Then circle.

❶ _7_ six / (seven) / ten

❷ ___ three / eight / five

❸ ___ six / nine / eight

2 Connect the questions and answers.

1 What's your name?   **a** I'm seven years old.

2 How old are you?   **b** Yes, I am.

3 Are you from Russia?   **c** I'm Alex.

4 Lesson 1 · VOCABULARY ·

1 Look and check (✓).

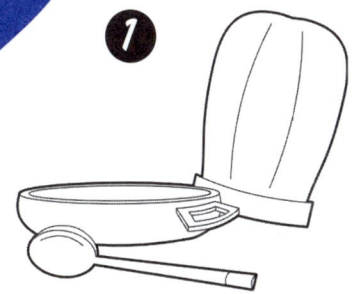

①

cook ✓
artist ○

②

actor ○
farmer ○

③

teacher ○
artist ○

④

teacher ○
farmer ○

⑤

doctor ○
cook ○

⑥

doctor ○
actor ○

2 Find and circle the word. Then circle the picture.

t	m	c	e	a	l	v
x	t	k	t	o	r	t
f	a	r	m	e	r	f

①  ②

DICTIONARY
page D4

27

Unit 4 · Lesson 2 · GRAMMAR

1 Match the pictures and sentences. Then look and circle.

a He's / She's a farmer. ○

b He's / She's a cook. ○

c He's / She's a doctor. ○

d He's / She's a teacher. ○

2 Look and connect.

He's
He isn't   a farmer.

His
Her   name's Sue.

His
Her   name's Joe.

She's
She isn't   a doctor.

Lesson 3 ·SPELLING·

1 Read. Then underline s, y, f, and x.

This is a farmer.
His name's Yuri.

This is his sister and this is a fox.

2 Write s, y, f, or x.

1 Thi___ i___ a ___armer.
   Hi___ name'___ ___uri.

2 Thi___ i___
   hi___ ___i___ter.

3 Thi___ i___
   a ___o___.

Lesson 4

MAKE I'M SORRY CARDS

Accept apologies!

VALUES PROJECT

You need: paper, pencils

Fold the paper.

Draw and color.

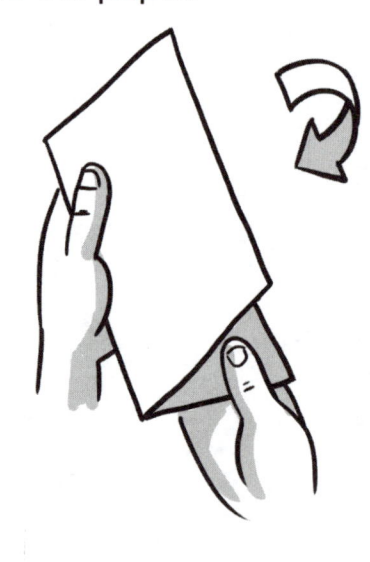

Write: **I'm sorry** and your name.

Give and accept apologies!

I'm sorry, Mom.

It's OK.

About Me
When was the last time you said *sorry* to someone?

Lesson 5

VOCABULARY

1 Look and circle.

1. **taekwondo instructor** (circled) / singer

2. engineer / soccer player

3. inventor / dancer

4. dancer / taekwondo instructor

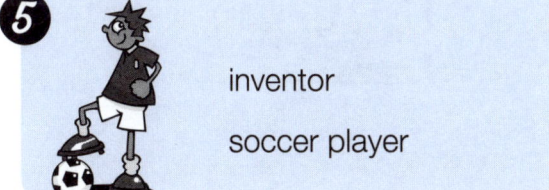
5. inventor / soccer player

6. singer / dancer

2 Look at Activity 1. Read and check (✓).

1 He's a taekwondo instructor.
   a  b  c

2 He's an engineer.
   a  b  c

3 He's a singer.
   a  b  c

DICTIONARY page D4

31

Lesson 6

GRAMMAR

1 Read. Then look and connect.

1  Is she an artist?

Yes, she is.
No, she isn't.

2  Is he an artist?

Yes, he is.
No, he isn't.

3  Is he a farmer?

Yes, he is.
No, he isn't.

4  Is she an inventor?

Yes, she is.
No, she isn't.

TRACK 42

2 Listen, read, and check (✓).

Is he an artist?
Is he an actor?

1 No, no, no, he isn't. ◯   Yes, yes, yes, he is. ◯

Is he a farmer with a big, red tractor?

2 No, no, no, he isn't! ◯   Yes, yes, yes, he is! ◯

Is she a singer?
Is she a cook?

3 No, no, no, she isn't. ◯   Yes, yes, yes, she is. ◯

Is she a teacher with a big, green book?

4 No, no, no, she isn't! ◯   Yes, yes, yes, she is! ◯

32

Lessons 7 and 8

LET'S VISIT SPAIN

1 Read. Then circle **True** or **False**.

1 Juan is a dancer.   True / (False)

2 Paella is a traditional dish from Spain.   True / False

3 Fernanda is an artist.   True / False

4 Fernanda is famous.   True / False

5 Her favorite artist is Joan Miró.   True / False

2 Now read page 50 of your Student's Book and check your answers.

3 Draw a famous person from your country. Then circle and write.

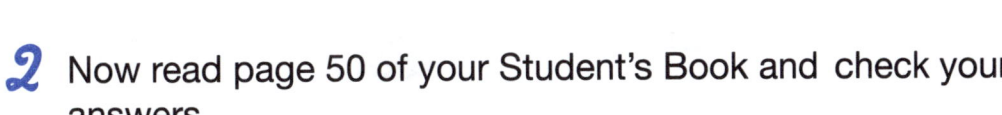

artist

cook

soccer player

singer

This is a / an _____ from my country.

His / Her name's _____.

33

PLAY TIME

Read and connect the dots in the correct order. Then write the number.

a fish ... panda ... pen ... eraser ... mom ... book
What's the number? _5_

b monkey ... tiger ... backpack ... pencil ... grandpa ... ruler ... backpack
What's the number? ___

c octopus ... elephant ... monkey ... tiger ... fish ... panda
What's the number? ___

d desk ... pencil case ... clock ... board ... clock ... window ... door
What's the number? ___

34

PLAY TIME

Look at the pictures and check (✓).

	1	2			1	2
a doctor	○	✓	f cook	○	○
b teacher	○	○	g artist	○	○
c engineer	○	○	h soccer player	○	○
d actor	○	○	i singer	○	○
e farmer	○	○	j inventor	○	○

UNIT 5

Lesson 1

VOCABULARY

1 Connect the pictures and words.

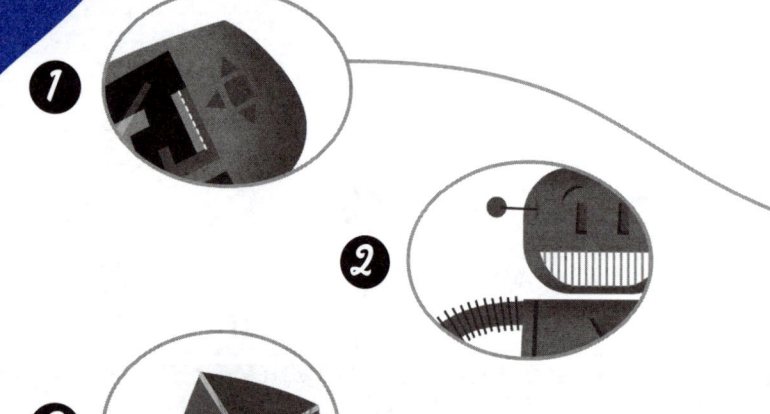
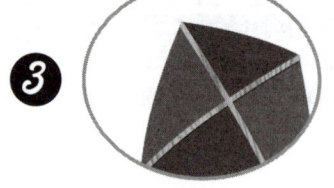
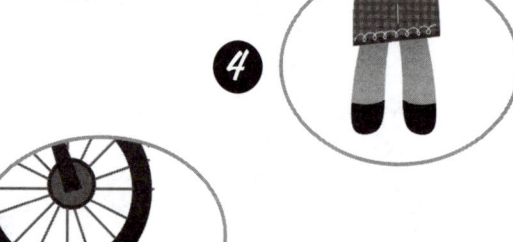
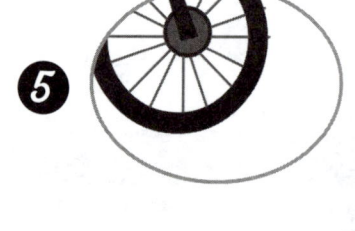

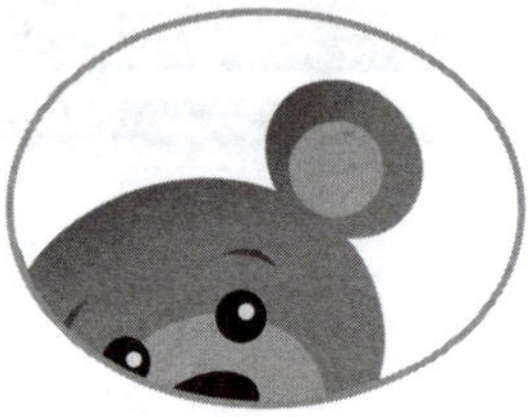

a doll

b computer game

c teddy bear

d robot

e bike

f kite

2 Circle the words. Then draw the missing toy from Activity 1.

DICTIONARY
page D5

Lesson 2

GRAMMAR

1 Look. Then circle and write.

1 It's a / (They're) computer game_s_.

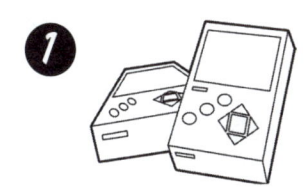

2 It's a / They're robot___.

3 It's a / They're bike___.

4 It's a / They're doll___.

5 It's a / They're teddy bear___.

6 It's a / They're kite___.

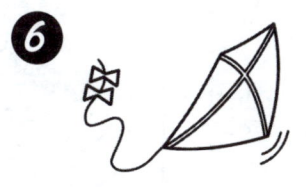

2 Look. Then connect the questions and answers.

1 What are they?   **a** Yes, she is.

2 What is it?   **b** They're kites.

3 Is she a teacher?   **c** It's a bike.

UNIT 5 — Lesson 3 — SPELLING

1 Read. Then underline <u>w</u>, <u>k</u>, <u>g</u>, <u>q</u>, and <u>r</u>.

1. What's in window 1?
   She's my grandma. She's the queen.

2. What's in window 2?
   It's the cook. He's a robot.

3. What's in window 3?
   He's my grandpa ... and it's my bike!

2 Write w, k, g, q, or r.

1 ___hat's in ___indo___ 1?

2 She's my ___ ___andma. She's the ___ueen.

3 It's the coo___. He's a ___obot.

Lesson 4

MAKE AN INVITATION
Play together!

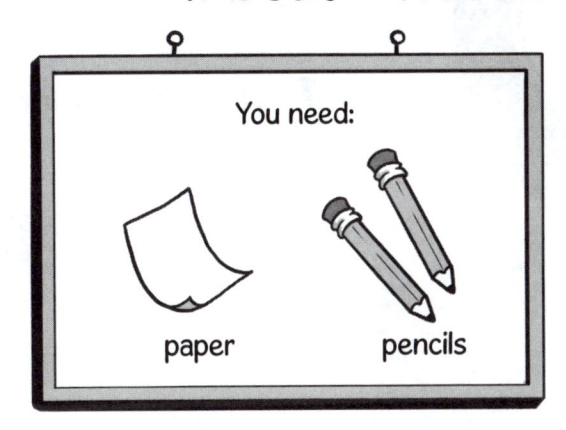

VALUES PROJECT

You need:
paper   pencils

Write: **Let's play together!**

Decorate. Write your name.

Invite a friend to play.

Hi. Let's play together.

OK.

Play together.

About Me
What games do you play with your friends?

UNIT 5 — Lesson 5

VOCABULARY

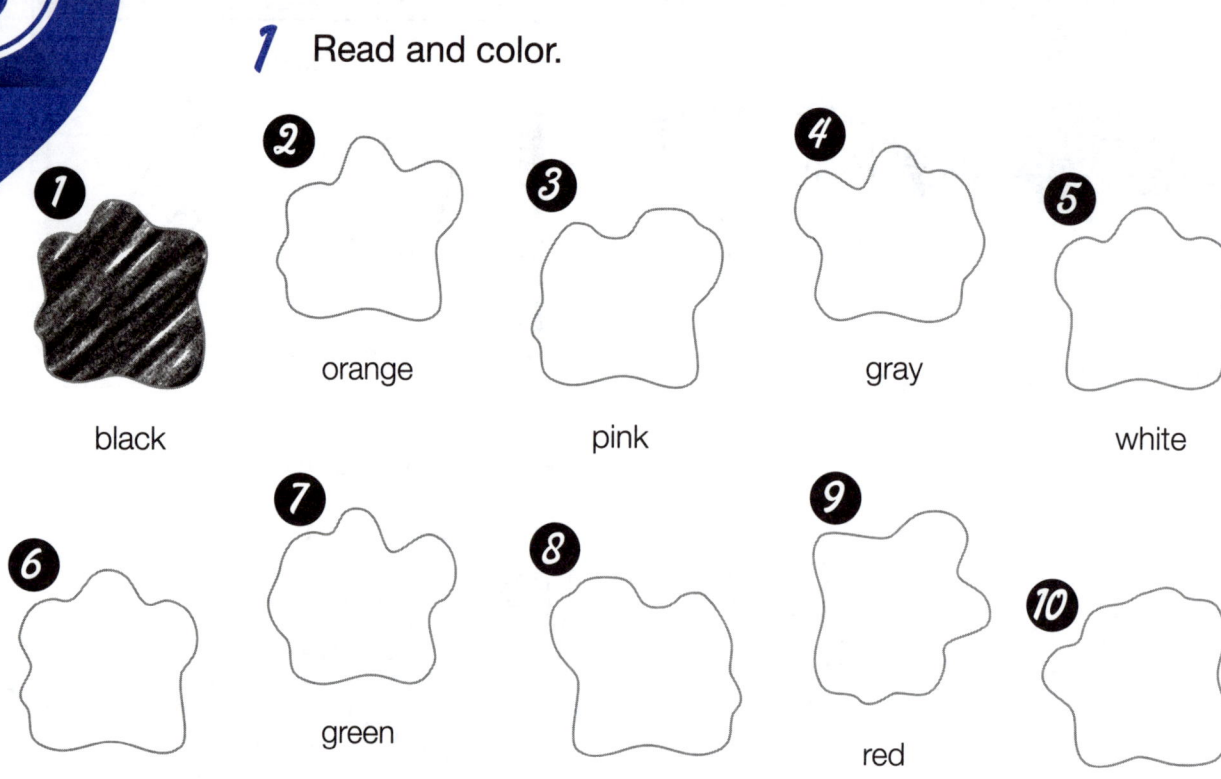

1 Read and color.

1. black
2. orange
3. pink
4. gray
5. white
6. brown
7. green
8. blue
9. red
10. yellow

2 Color the animals their real colors. Then read and check (✓).

1 pandas

They're green and white.
True ◯   False ◯

2 elephants

They're gray.
True ◯   False ◯

3 tigers

They're black and green.
True ◯   False ◯

DICTIONARY page D5

40

Lesson 6

GRAMMAR

1 Look. Then read and circle.

1
Are they gray kites?
Yes, they are. / No, they aren't.

2
Are they gray robots?
Yes, they are. / No, they aren't.

3
Are they black bikes?
Yes, they are. / No, they aren't.

4
Are they black teddy bears?
Yes, they are. / No, they aren't.

TRACK 53

2 Listen and circle. Then color.

1 Are they green teddy bears?
Yes, they are. / No, they aren't.

2 Are they blue teddy bears?
Yes, they are. / No, they aren't.

3 Are they yellow teddy bears?
Yes, they are. / No, they aren't.

The teddy bears are yellow
They aren't green or blue,
The teddy bears are yellow
And they are for you!

UNIT 5

Lessons 7 and 8

LET'S VISIT EGYPT

1 Use the key to color the picture. Then write.

| **1** = yellow | **2** = red | **3** = pink | **4** = brown | **5** = green |
| **6** = blue | **7** = black | **8** = orange | **9** = white | **10** = gray |

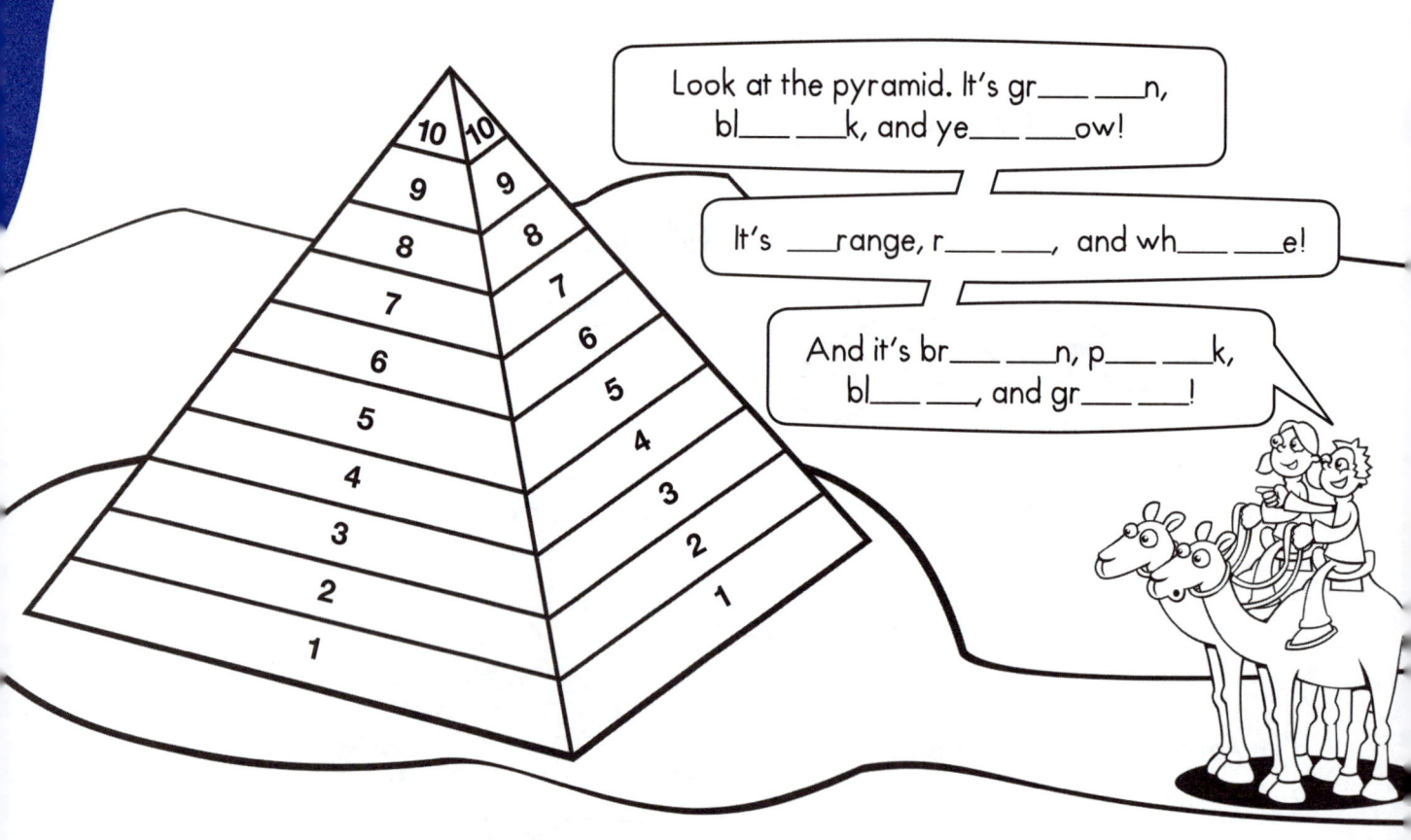

Look at the pyramid. It's gr___ ___n, bl___ ___k, and ye___ ___ow!

It's ___range, r___ ___, and wh___ ___e!

And it's br___ ___n, p___ ___k, bl___ ___, and gr___ ___!

2 Color the camels any color. Then read and circle.

1 Are they pandas?
Yes, they are. / No, they aren't.

2 Are they red camels?
Yes, they are. / No, they aren't.

3 Are they brown camels?
Yes, they are. / No, they aren't.

Lesson **1**

· VOCABULARY ·

1 Look and check (✓).

1. 
cat ○
bird ✓

2. 
horse ○
dog ○

3. 
dog ○
bird ○

4. 
horse ○
turtle ○

5. 
cat ○
rabbit ○

6. 
cat ○
turtle ○

2 Use the key to color the pictures. Then write.

1 = red
2 = black
3 = yellow
4 = white
5 = blue

1 It's a ___e___, ___el___ ___ ___,
and ___l___e ___ir___.

2 It's a ___l___ ___k and
___h___ ___e ___o___.

DICTIONARY
page D6

43

UNIT 6   Lesson 2   · GRAMMAR ·

1 Match the pictures and sentences.

a I don't have a fish. ◯   **c** I don't have a dog. ◯

b I have a rabbit. ◯   **d** I have a horse. ◯

2 Write true sentences about you.

| have   don't have |

1 I _____ a dog.   5 I _____ a rabbit.

2 I _____ a cat.   6 I _____ a horse.

3 I _____ a sister.   7 I _____ a bike.

4 I _____ a brother.   8 I _____ a teddy bear.

Lesson 3

· SPELLING ·

1 Read. Then underline <u>l</u>, <u>j</u>, <u>z</u>, <u>v</u>, and <u>n</u>.

1. Zebra is a soccer player. He's number five.

2. Turtle is an inventor. This is his van.

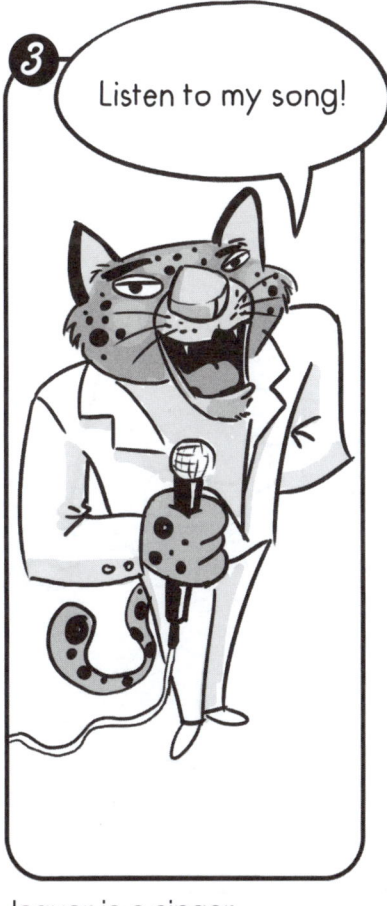

3. Listen to my song!
Jaguar is a singer.

2 Write *l*, *j*, *z*, *v*, or *n*.

1 ___ebra is a soccer p___ayer.

2 This is his ___an.

3 ___aguar is a si___ger.

45

UNIT 6

Lesson 4

MAKE A PET CHART

Be kind to your pet!

VALUES PROJECT

You need:
paper, pencils

Choose a pet and draw it.

Draw your pet's things.

Write: **I love my** _____.

Make a class chart.

About Me
Do you have a pet? What do you do to take care of it?

Lesson 5

·VOCABULARY·

1 Write. Then read and color the animals.

~~snake~~   mouse   iguana   frog   spider   hamster

1. I have a green sn_a_ _k_ _e_.
2. I have a gray m___ ___ ___ ___.
3. I have a green ig___ ___ ___.
4. I have a red fr___ ___.
5. I have a black sp___ ___ ___ ___.
6. I have an orange h___ ___ ___ ___ ___ ___.

2 Draw yourself with an animal from Activity 1. Color the animal. Then circle and write.

I have a / an _____ _____.

DICTIONARY page D6

47

Lesson 6

GRAMMAR

1 Write. Then color your answers.

Do   **have**

| Yes, I do. = green | No, I don't. = red |

1. ____Do____ you have a bike?
2. Do you _____ a computer game?
3. Do you _____ a fish?
4. _____ you have a rabbit?
5. _____ you have a brother?
6. Do you _____ a sister?

TRACK 63

2 Listen, read, and connect in the correct order.

- Do you have a cat?
- Do you have a spider?
- Do you have a hamster?
- Do you have a tiger?
- Do you have a frog?
- Yes, I do!
- Do you have a rabbit?
- No, I don't!
- Do you have a fish?
- Do you have a dog?

48

Lessons 7 and 8

LET'S VISIT MEXICO

1 Read. Then look and write.

Yes, it is.   No, it isn't.

1. Is it from Mexico?
_____.

2. Is it from Mexico?
_____.

3. Is it from Mexico?
_____.

2 Write the words. Then draw.

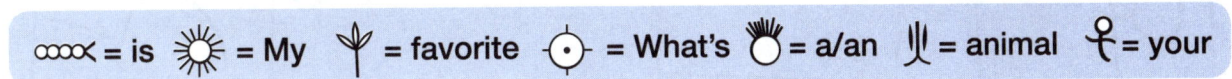

∞∞∞ = is   ☀ = My   ⚘ = favorite   ⊙ = What's   ◯ = a/an   ⫯ = animal   ⚲ = your

⊙   ⚲   ⚘   ⫯

What's _____ _____ _____ _____?

☀   ⚘   ⫯   ∞∞∞   ◯

_____ _____ _____ _____ _____.

_____.

PLAY TIME

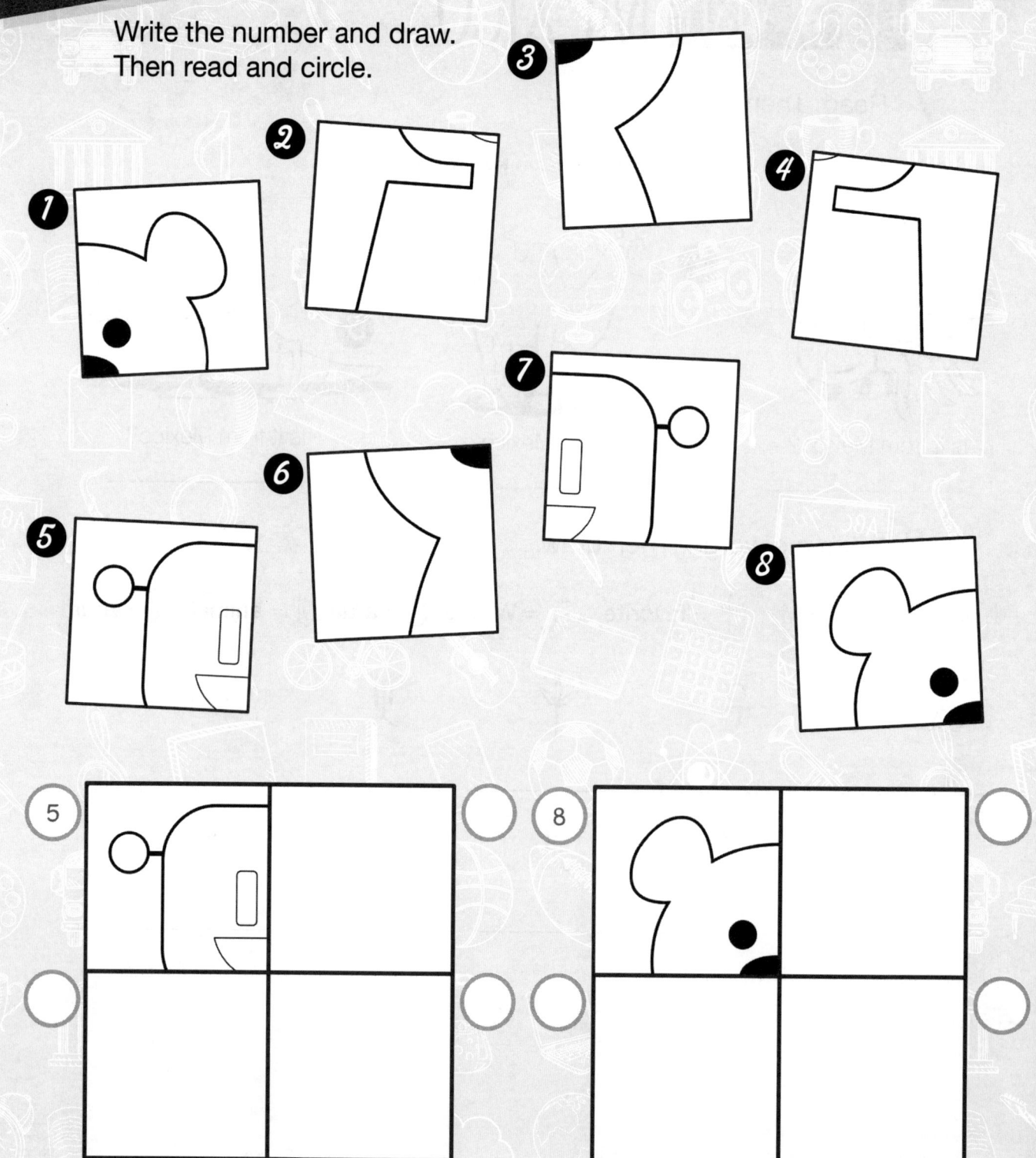

UNIT 5

Write the number and draw.
Then read and circle.

a It's a computer game. / robot.

b It's a teddy bear. / doll.

PLAY TIME

UNIT 6

Find and circle the words. Then write.

1. cat

2. _____

3. _____

i	g	u	a	n	a	b	r
x	h	s	e	w	c	o	e
d	f	n	i	w	a	q	f
z	h	a	m	s	t	e	r
r	o	k	o	p	l	b	o
a	r	e	u	i	d	o	g
b	s	g	s	d	r	e	w
b	e	p	e	e	d	f	x
i	a	b	i	r	d	v	u
t	u	r	t	l	e	t	d

4. _____
5. _____
6. _____
7. _____
8. _____ 
9. _____ 
10. _____ 
11. _____ 
12. _____

51

Unit 7 Lesson 1

VOCABULARY

1 Match the words to the picture.

1 hair — d
2 nose
3 ears
4 eyes
5 mouth
6 teeth

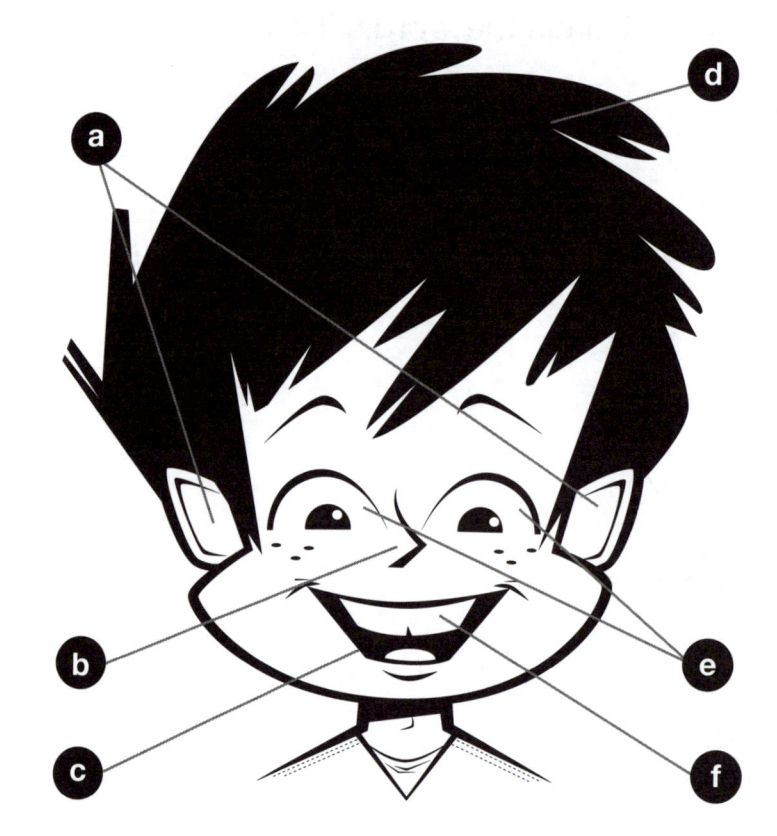

2 Write. Then draw a picture of your face. Connect the words to the picture.

1 h _a_ _i_ _r_

2 e___es

3 ea___s

4 n___s___

5 m___ ___th

6 t___ ___th

DICTIONARY page D7

Lesson 2

· GRAMMAR ·

1 Use the key to color the pictures. Then write.

1 = brown   2 = blue   3 = black

1 He ___has___ ___blue___ eyes.   **3** He _____ _____ hair.
2 She _____ _____ eyes.   **4** She _____ _____ hair.

2 Find and paste a picture of a person's face. Then write.

| He | She | brown |
| black | blue | green |

_____ _____ _____ hair.
_____ _____ _____ eyes.

53

Lesson 3

SPELLING

1 Read. Then underline _ll_ and _zz_.

1
Hello. I'm Ella.

2
This is Izzy. She's a doll.

3
Izzy's dizzy!

2 Write _ll_ or _zz_.

1 He___ ___o.
I'm E___ ___a.

2 This is I___ ___y.
She's a do___ ___.

3 I___ ___y's
di___ ___y!

Lesson 4

MAKE A BE CLEAN CHART
Be clean!

VALUES PROJECT

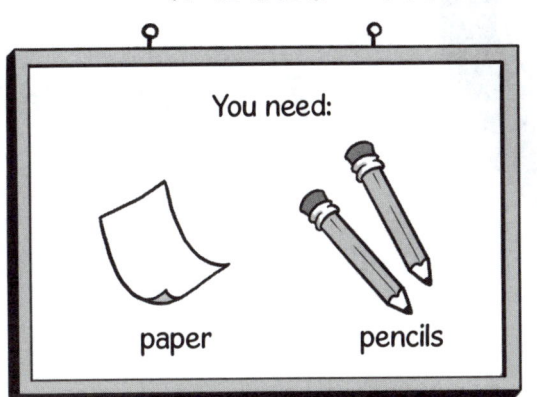

You need:
- paper
- pencils

Make a chart and draw.

Check (✓) the chart for one day.

Count and complete.

- I brush my teeth _____ time(s).
- I brush my hair _____ time(s).
- I wash my hands _____ time(s).
- I wash my face _____ time(s).

About Me
Why is it important to be clean?

UNIT 7 — Lesson 5

VOCABULARY

1 Find and write. Then match the words to the picture.

1 nsdha = <u>h</u> <u>a</u> <u>n</u> <u>d</u> <u>s</u>

2 steo = ___ ___ ___ ___

3 mars = ___ ___ ___ ___

4 efte = ___ ___ ___ ___

5 grfneis = ___ ___ ___ ___ ___ ___

6 glse = ___ ___ ___ ___

TRACK 73

2 Listen and write.

1 Shake your ___arms___,

2 Shake your _____,

3 Clap your _____,

4 And stamp your _____.

Arms, legs, hands, feet!
Arms, legs, hands, feet!

5 Touch your _____,

6 Touch your _____,

7 Close your _____,

8 And touch your _____.

Ears, toes, eyes, nose!
Ears, toes, eyes, nose!

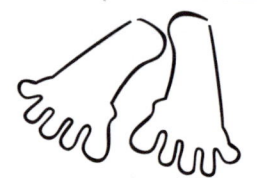

DICTIONARY page D7

56

Lesson 6

GRAMMAR

1 Read. Then look and write.

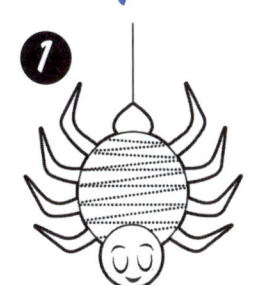

Yes, it does.   **No, it doesn't.**

1 Does it have eight legs?
   _____.

2 Does it have hands?
   _____.

3 Does it have ten fingers?
   _____.

4 Does it have ears?
   _____.

2 Draw the faces of two friends. Then write.

This is a boy in my class.

His name's _____.

This is a girl in my class.

Her name's _____.

1 __Does__ he have black hair?

   _____, he _____.

2 Does he _____ three ears?

   _____.

3 _____ she have brown hair?

   _____, she _____.

4 Does she _____ green eyes?

   _____.

57

UNIT 7

Lessons 7 and 8

LET'S VISIT INDIA

1 Write. Then read and color.

black
elephant
orange
dancer
white

1 This is an el ___ ___ ___ ___ ___ ___ from India. It has o___ ___ ___ ___ ___ and w___ ___ ___ ___ ears.

2 This is a ___ ___ ___ ___ ___ ___ from India. He has b___ ___ ___ ___ hair.

2 Answer the questions for you.

Yes, I do.   No, I don't.

1 Do you have brown eyes? _____.

2 Do you have brown hair? _____.

3 Do you have blue eyes? _____.

4 Do you have black hair? _____.

Lesson 1

· VOCABULARY ·

1 Write. Then connect the words and pictures.

1 p_o_ _o_ l

2 p___ ___k

3 m___ ___l

4 st___d___ ___m

5 ___ ___ ___ool

6 z___ ___

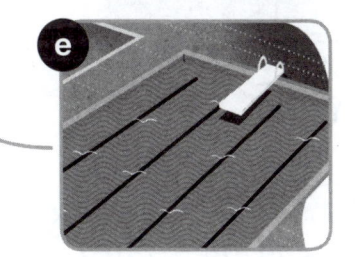

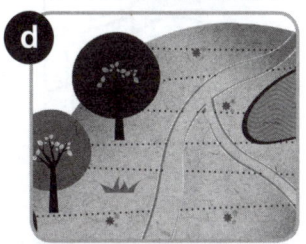

a
b
c
d
e
f   SCHOOL

2 Circle the words. Then look at Activity 1 and draw the missing place.

zoo mall pool stadium park

DICTIONARY page D8

Lesson 2

GRAMMAR

1 Look, read, and circle.

1 There's / (There isn't) a mall.
2 There's / There isn't a stadium.
3 There's / There isn't a school.
4 There's / There isn't a park.
5 There's / There isn't a pool.
6 There's / There isn't a zoo.

2 Write true sentences for you.

there's   there isn't

In my backpack ...
1 _____ a doll.
2 _____ a ruler.
3 _____ a pencil case.
4 _____ an eraser.
5 _____ a book.

Lesson 3

· SPELLING ·

1 Read. Then underline *ss* and *ff*.

❶

❷

Happy birthday!

❸

Oh, no! Look at my dress.

This is a giraffe, and this is her class.

It's the giraffe's birthday. She has a grass cake.

2 Write *ss* or *ff*.

1 This is a gira___ ___e.

2 She has a gra___ ___ cake.

3 Look at my dre___ ___.

61

UNIT 8

Lesson 4

MAKE A LITTER POSTER

Don't drop litter!

VALUES PROJECT

You need:
- paper
- glue
- pencils
- recyclable materials

Draw a trash can.

Paste recyclable materials around the trash can.

Write: **Don't drop litter!**

Put your poster in school.

Don't drop litter!

About Me
Where are the trash cans in your school?

62

Lesson 5 ·VOCABULARY·

1 Find and circle the words.

① ch(beach)ch

② klakeka

③ reetreet

④ wflowerfl

⑤ rvrriverev

⑥ tnimountainnt

TRACK 84

2 Listen and write.

Fly, fly up to the sky
Look at the world
From way up high.

1 I see _____mountains_____   I see a park

2 I see _____   5 I see a _____

3 I see a _____   I see you

4 And a yellow _____.   6 And a red _____.

DICTIONARY page D8

63

Lesson 6

GRAMMAR

1 Follow the path. Then read and check (✓).

	Yes, there is.	No, there isn't.
1 Is there a beach?	○	○
2 Is there a mountain?	○	○
3 Is there a river?	○	○
4 Is there a flower?	○	○
5 Is there a lake?	○	○

2 Read and write the answers.

Yes, there is.   No, there isn't.

In your classroom …

1 is there a clock? _____.

2 is there a spider? _____.

3 is there a board? _____.

Lessons 7 and 8

LET'S VISIT THE UK

1 Look, read, and cross out (✗) the mistakes. Then write correct sentences.

1 The ~~stadium~~ is old.   The castle is old_____.

2 There's a river in the park.   _____.

3 There's a mountain in the park. _____.

2 Read and draw.

This is a park in the UK. There's a lake. There's a tree.

There's a boy in the park. There's a girl in the park. She has a kite.

PLAY TIME

UNIT 7

Look and complete the puzzles. Then read and write the answers.

a Does it have fingers and toes?

_____Yes_____, _____

_____.

1 f i n g e r s

b Does it have hair?

_____, _____

_____.

c Does it have four legs?

_____, _____

_____.

66

PLAY TIME

UNIT 8

Toss a coin and move your game piece. Say the sentence or answer the question.

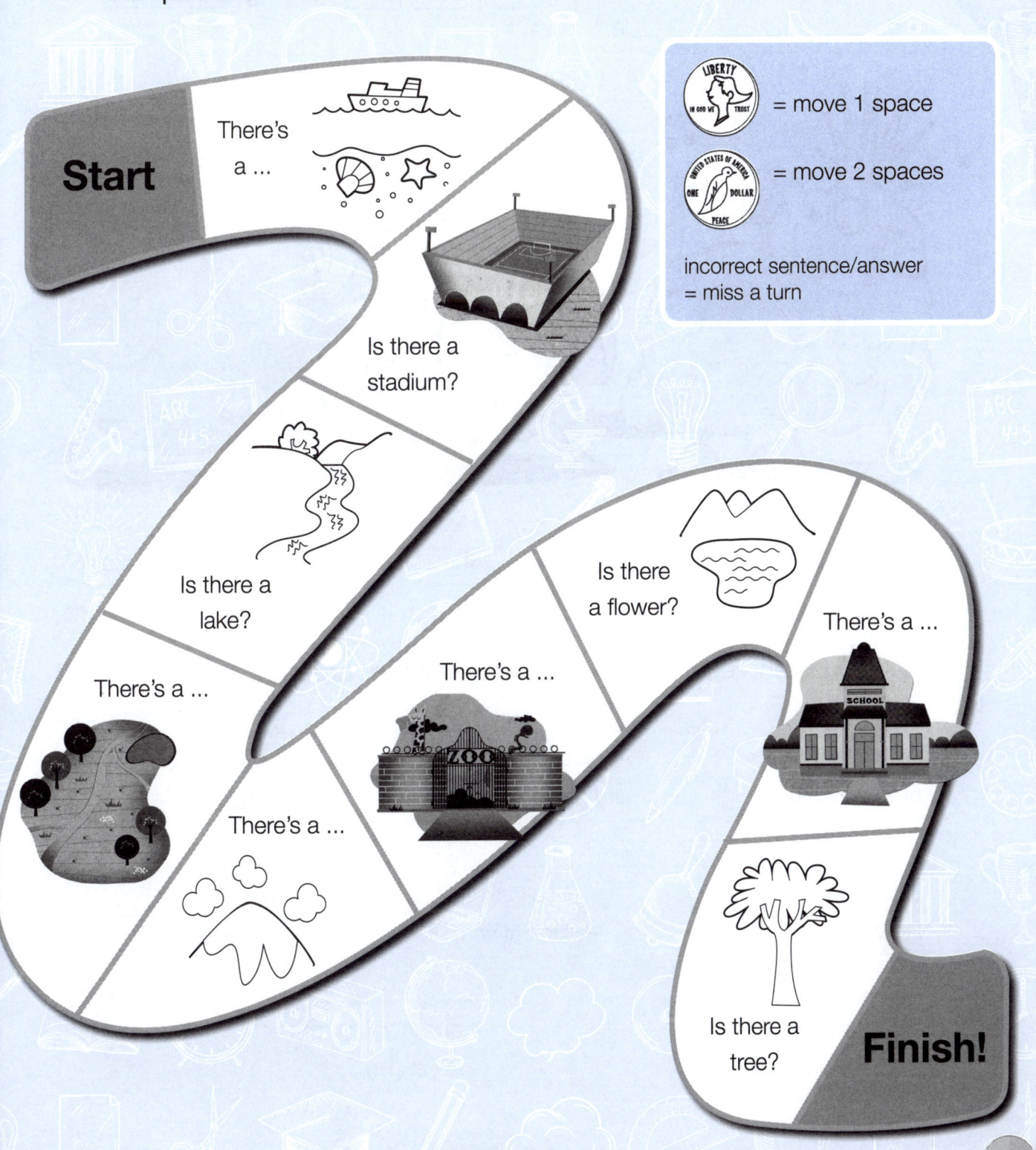

= move 1 space
= move 2 spaces

incorrect sentence/answer = miss a turn

Start

There's a ...

Is there a stadium?

Is there a lake?

There's a ...

There's a ...

There's a ...

Is there a flower?

There's a ...

Is there a tree?

Finish!

67

UNIT 9 Lesson 1 · VOCABULARY ·

1 Look and write.

1 p__ __ __ __ __ __le

2 b__ __ __n__

3 p__ __ __

4 o__a__ge

5 __pp__ __

6 __ __ __ __ __ __ __l__n

TRACK 87

2 Listen, read, and connect in the correct order.

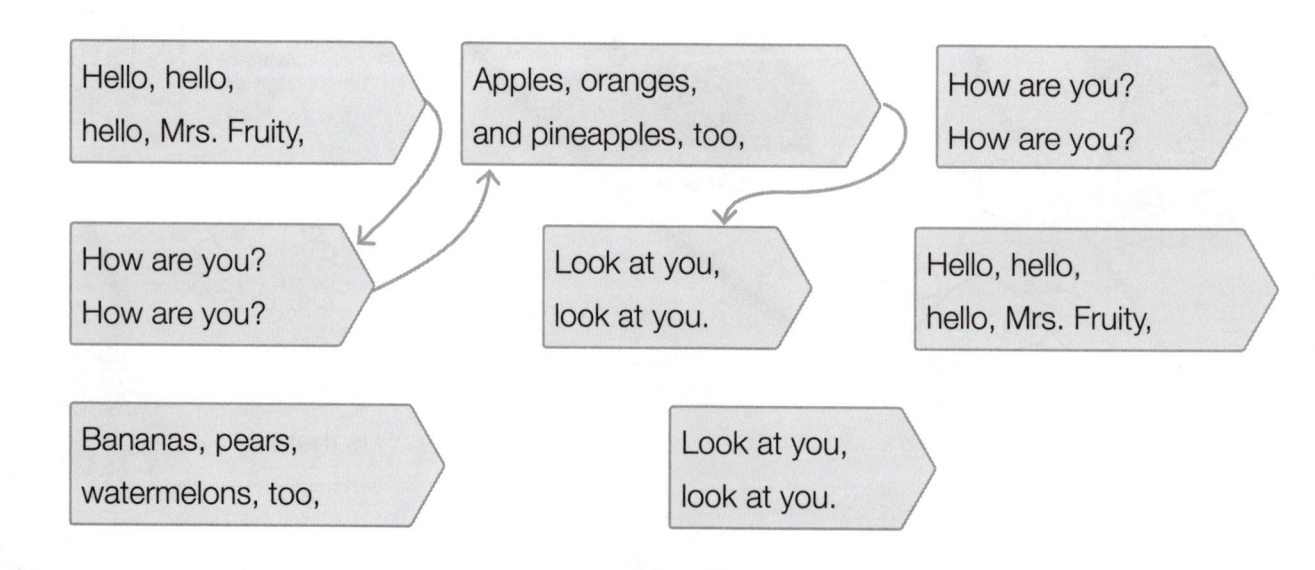

| Hello, hello, hello, Mrs. Fruity, |

| Apples, oranges, and pineapples, too, |

| How are you? How are you? |

| How are you? How are you? |

| Look at you, look at you. |

| Hello, hello, hello, Mrs. Fruity, |

| Bananas, pears, watermelons, too, |

| Look at you, look at you. |

DICTIONARY page D9

Lesson 2

GRAMMAR

1 Look, read, and circle.

1 There are five bananas. / oranges.
2 There's one monkey. / bird.
3 There are two birds. / robots.
4 There are three teddy bears. / watermelons.
5 There are two bananas. / dolls.

2 Look at Activity 1 and write.

There's a   There are

1 _____ bananas.   4 _____ teddy bears.
2 _____ watermelons.   5 _____ monkey.
3 _____ birds.

69

UNIT 9 Lesson 3 · SPELLING·

1 Read. Then underline *ch* and *sh*.

1 I have a chicken and a fish in my shopping cart. I don't have chips, and I don't have peaches or cherries.

2 Look, Dad! There are chips here.

3 There are peaches and cherries here!

2 Write *ch* or *sh*.

1 There's a ___ ___icken and a fi___ ___ in the ___ ___opping cart.

2 There are pea___ ___es and ___ ___erries here.

Lesson 4

MAKE A LOST PROPERTY BOX

Don't take others' things!

VALUES PROJECT

You need:
- sticky labels
- a marker
- paints
- a large box

Make name labels.

Label your things.

Make a lost property box.

Put others' things in the box.

About Me
What do you do if you find something on the street?

Lesson 5 · VOCABULARY ·

1 Write the words and numbers. Then count in order.

a ____16____ sixteen

b _____ fourteen

c 15 _____

d _____ nineteen

e 11 _____

f 20 _____

g 12 _____

h _____ thirteen

i 17 _____

j _____ eighteen

eleven, twelve, thirteen …

2 Add and write the number.

1 Four and ten is _____fourteen_____.
2 Three and ten is _____.
3 Ten and ten is _____.
4 Two and ten is _____.
5 Five and ten is _____.
6 Ten and one is _____.

3 Read and connect in the correct order. Then write.

thirteen… seventeen… eleven… fifteen… thirteen… eleven… fifteen… seventeen

• 11

13 •

15 •

17 •

There's a _____.

72 DICTIONARY page D9

Lesson 6

GRAMMAR

1 Add. Then write.

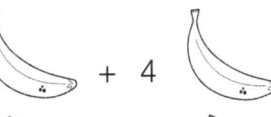

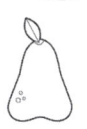

1 6 🍍 + 8 🍍 = There are _____fourteen_____ pineapples.

2 9 🍌 + 4 🍌 = There _____ _____ bananas.

3 6 🍐 + 5 🍐 = _____ are _____ pears.

2 Look at Activity 1 and complete the questions.

1 How many _____ _____ there?
There are thirteen.

2 How _____ _____ are _____?
There are eleven.

3 _____ _____ _____ are there?
There are fourteen.

3 Write the words. Then look and write the answers.

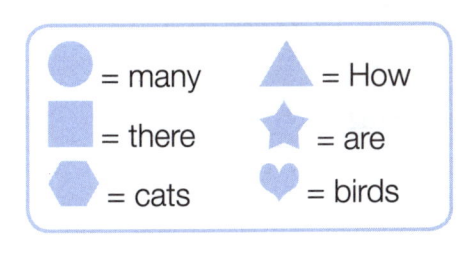

- ● = many
- ▲ = How
- ■ = there
- ★ = are
- ⬢ = cats
- ♥ = birds

▲ ● ⬢ ★ ■

1 ___How___ _____ _____ _____ _____?
There are _____.

▲ ● ♥ ★ ■

2 _____ _____ _____ _____ _____?
_____.

UNIT 9

Lessons 7 and 8

LET'S VISIT BRAZIL

1 Connect the dots. Then write.

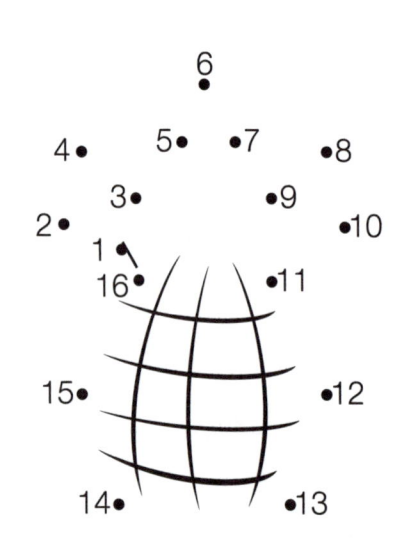

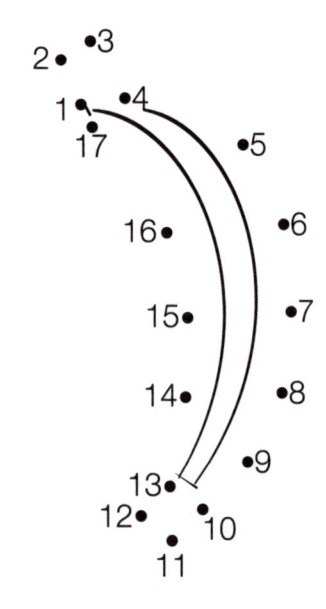

1 There's a _____.

2 _____.

2 Connect to make questions for Ana from page 112 of your Student's Book. Then write her answers.

1 Are you   a are you from in Brazil?
2 Where   b favorite fruits?
3 How old   c from Portugal?
4 What are your   d are you?

1 _____.
2 _____.
3 _____.
4 _____.

3 Now read pages 112 and 113 of your Student's Book and check your answers.

74

Lesson 1

VOCABULARY

1 Look at the pictures and check (✓).

	1	2
a There's a sofa.	○	✓
b There's a closet.	○	○
c There's a TV.	○	○
d There's a table.	○	○
e There's a chair.	○	○
f There's a bed.	○	○
g There's a teddy bear.	○	○
h There are books.	○	○

2 Look at Activity 1 and write.

Picture 1

There isn't a _____.

There isn't a _____.

Picture 2

There isn't a _____.

There isn't a _____.

DICTIONARY
page D10

75

Lesson 2

GRAMMAR

1 Look. Then read and circle.

1. The (teddy bear) / doll is (on) / under the chair.
2. The pencil / book is on / under the table.
3. The TV / cat is on / under the table.
4. The backpack / clock is on / in the closet.
5. Grandma / Grandpa is on / under the sofa.
6. The cat / dog is on / in the pool.

2 Choose a sentence. Check (✓) and draw.

1. There's a teddy bear on the bed. ◯

   There's a spider under the bed. ◯

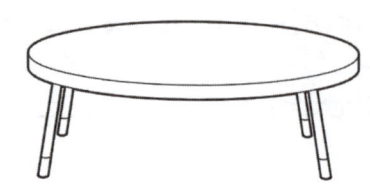

2. There's a flower on the table. ◯

   There's a clock under the table. ◯

76

Lesson 3

· SPELLING ·

1 Read. Then underline *nk* and *ng*.

1 A pink cake! That's great!

2 Thank you.

3 Let's sing a song.

Happy birthday to you!

2 Write *nk* or *ng*.

1 A pi___ ___ cake.

2 Tha___ ___ you.

3 Let's si___ ___ a so___ ___.

UNIT 10 — Lesson 4

MAKE A PENCIL BOX

Be neat!

VALUES PROJECT

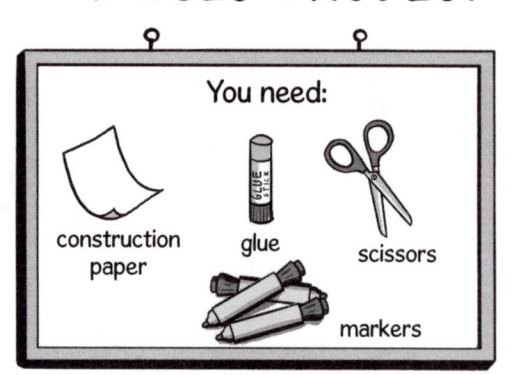

You need:
- construction paper
- glue
- scissors
- markers

Copy and draw this template.

Cut and glue the pencil box.

Decorate the pencil box.

Put your pens and pencils in the box.

About Me
How do you keep your things neat at home?

Lesson 5

·VOCABULARY·

1 Find and write. Then match the words to the picture.

1 gnilvi moro
  = liv_i_ _n_ _g_ _r_ _o_ om

2 nehcikt
  = __ __ __ __ __ __ __

3 dyra
  = __ __ __ __

4 erggaa
  = __ __ __ __ __ __

5 mobrode
  = __ __ __ __ __ __ __

6 rmoohtab
  = __ __ __ __ __ __ __ __

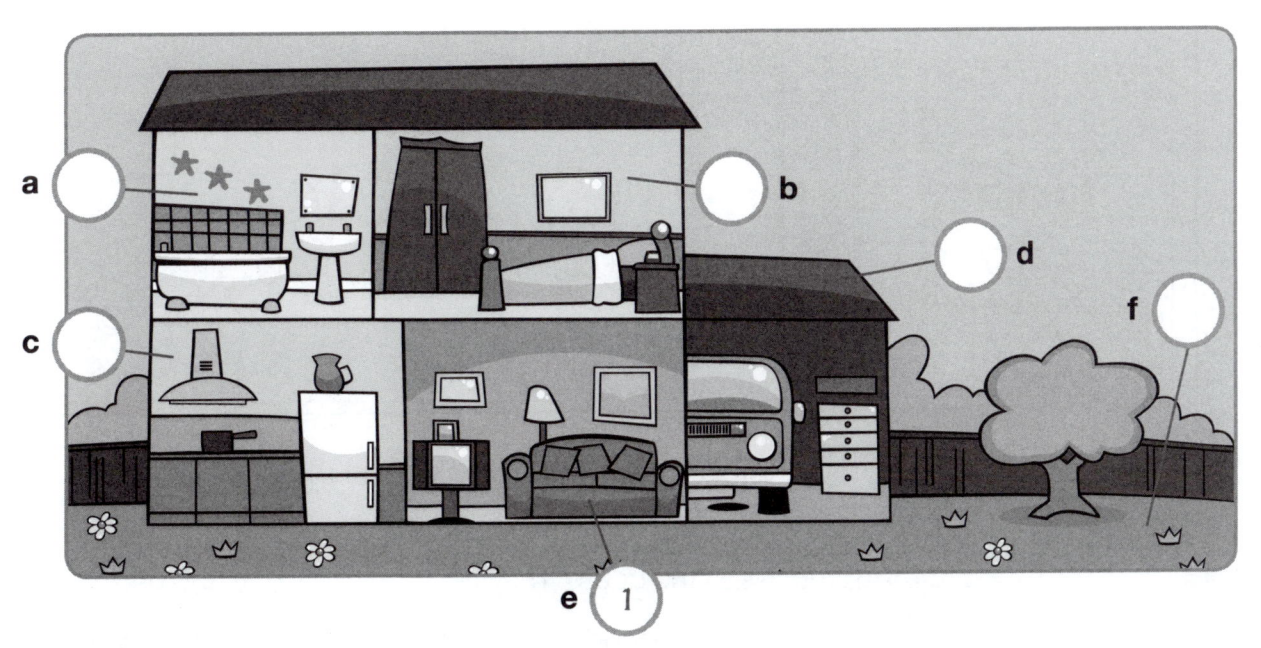

2 Read and connect.

The sofa is in the living room. The TV is in the kitchen.
The closet is in the garage.

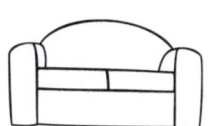

DICTIONARY
page D10

79

Lesson 6

GRAMMAR

1 Look. Then complete the questions and answers.

| Where are | Where's | in | on | under |

1 __Where are__ the dogs? They're ____in____ the bed.
2 _____ the teddy bear? It's _____ the chair.
3 _____ the monkeys? They're _____ the table.
4 _____ the robot? It's _____ the bed.
5 _____ the rabbit? It's _____ the closet.
6 _____ the dolls? They're _____ the sofa.

2 Look at Activity 1. Ask and answer with a friend.

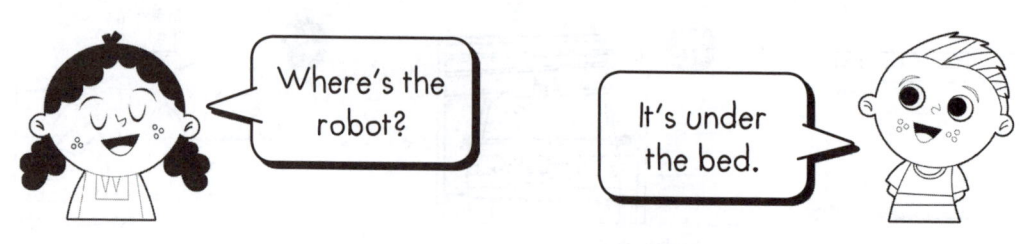

Where's the robot?

It's under the bed.

80

Lessons 7 and 8

LET'S VISIT JAPAN

1 Read. Then look and write.

1 Where's he from?
   He's from _____.
2 Is there a garden?
   _____.
3 Is there a garage?
   _____.
4 How many trees are there?
   There are _____.

2 Draw your house. Then write.

- living room
- bedroom
- bathroom
- kitchen
- garage
- yard
- tree
- flower
- There's
- There isn't
- There are

This is my house. There's _____
_____.

81

PLAY TIME

UNIT 9

1 Look and check (✓) the things in the picture.

apples ✓	bananas ◯	watermelons ◯	pears ◯
oranges ◯	pineapples ◯	trees ◯	flowers ◯
dog ◯	cat ◯	dancers ◯	mountains ◯
books ◯	doctors ◯	hats ◯	elephants ◯

2 Look at Activity 1. Write sentences using *There are*.

1 <u>There are apples</u>_____.
2 _____.
3 _____.
4 _____.
5 _____.
6 _____.
7 _____.
8 _____.

82

PLAY TIME

UNIT 10

Look and complete the puzzle.

1
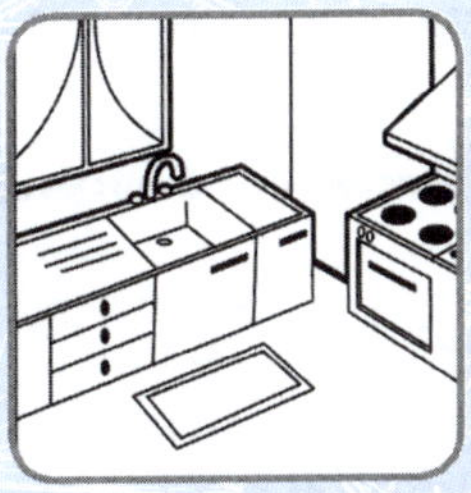

2
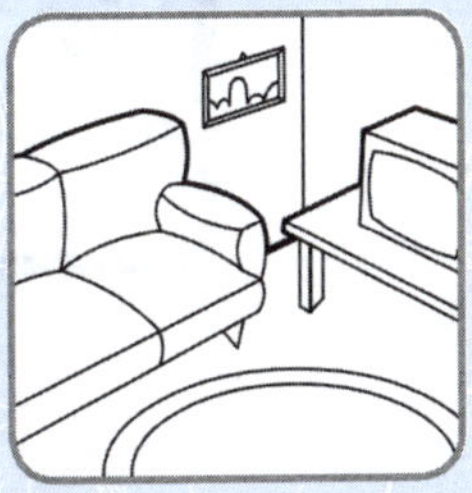

4
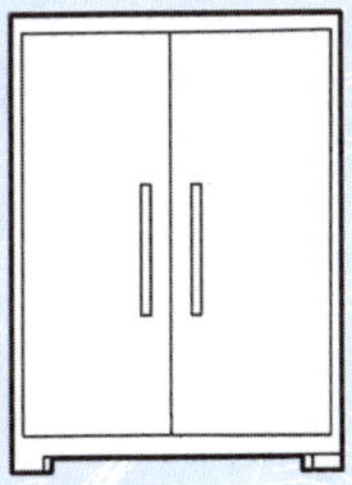

3
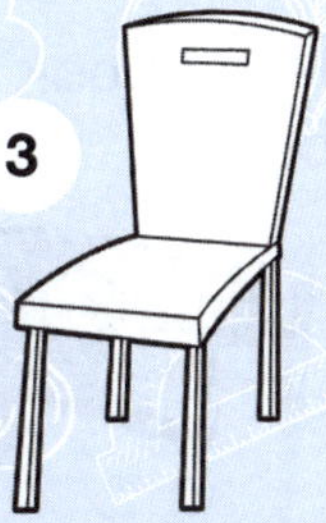

6
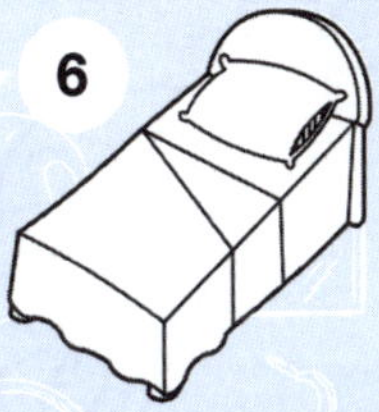

5
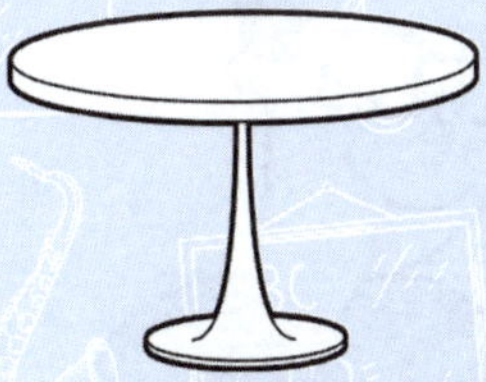

7
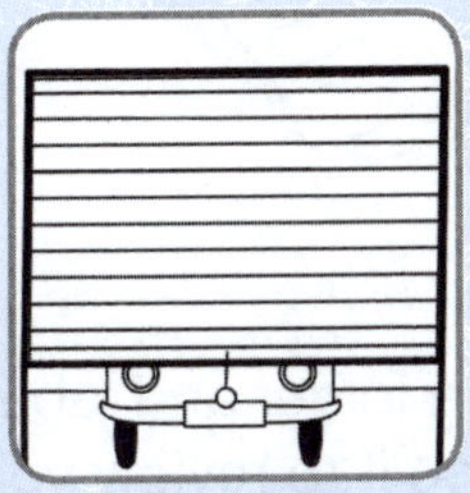

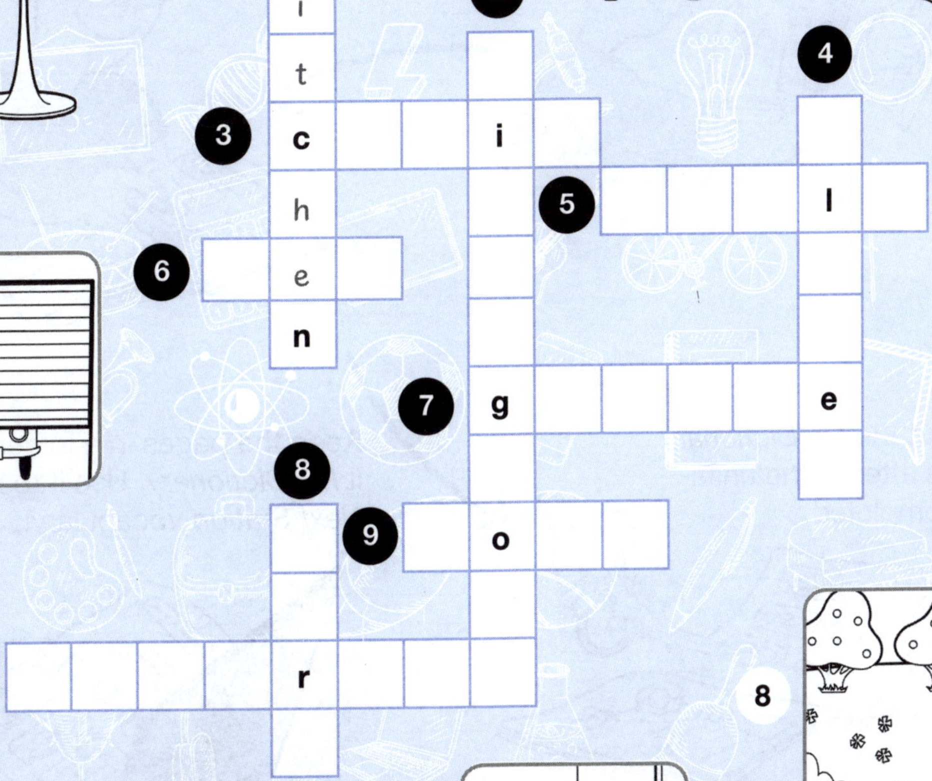

8
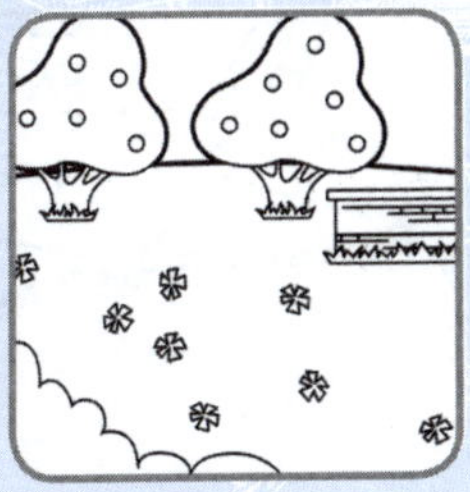

9
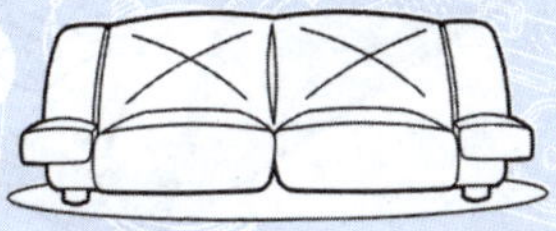

10
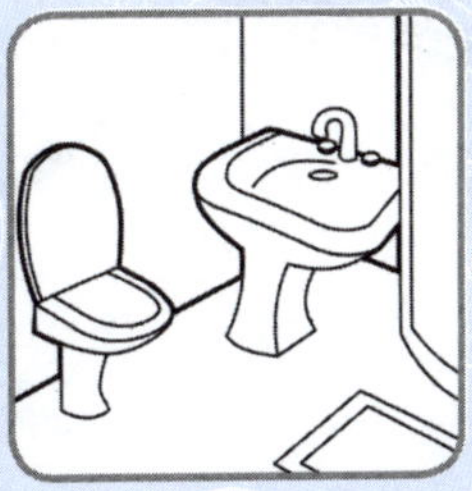

MY DICTIONARY

How to Make Your Dictionary

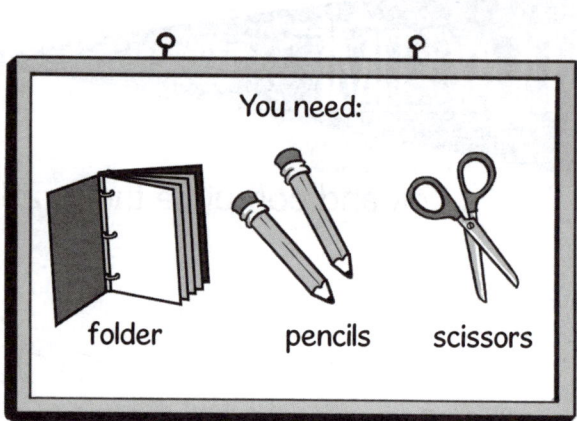

You need:

folder   pencils   scissors

Open your *Next Station* Workbook at the *My Dictionary* section.

Complete the *My Dictionary* pages for the unit.

Cut out the *My Dictionary* pages after all the units are completed.

Keep the pages in a folder and label it *My Dictionary*. Use it to review your *Next Station* vocabulary!

·MY DICTIONARY·

Page 4 Read and draw your friends.

Hello.   Hi.   Goodbye.   Bye.

Page 8 Read and draw.

mom    dad    grandma

grandpa   brother   sister

D1

MY DICTIONARY

Page 11 Read and draw.

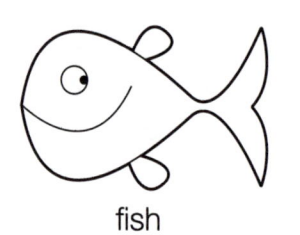

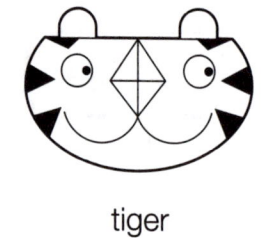

fish tiger elephant octopus

panda monkey

Page 15 Complete the picture.

clock
board
door
window
pencil case
desk

MY DICTIONARY

Page 20 Read and complete the numbers.

8	5	4	9	1
eight	five	four	nine	one

10	3	2	7	6
ten	three	two	seven	six

Page 24 Read and draw.

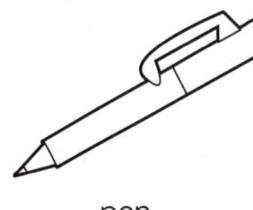

pen 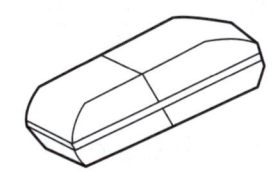   eraser    backpack

pencil   book   ruler

MY DICTIONARY

Page 27 Read and connect.

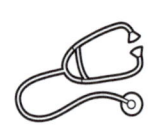

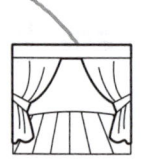

actor farmer artist cook teacher doctor

Page 31 Cross out (X) the one that's different. Then circle the word.

(dancer) / inventor

soccer player / taekwondo instructor

singer / dancer

engineer / soccer player

MY DICTIONARY

UNIT 5

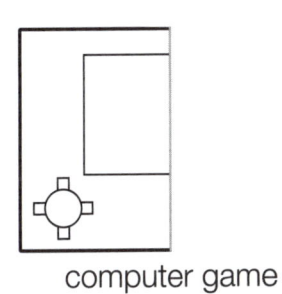

Page 36 Read and draw.

doll    robot   computer game    teddy bear

bike 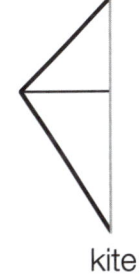   kite

Page 40 Color the objects in alphabetical order.

| 1 = red | 2 = yellow | 3 = blue | 4 = green | 5 = pink |
| 6 = brown | 7 = gray | 8 = white | 9 = black | 10 = orange |

bike    doll 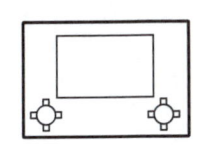   computer game 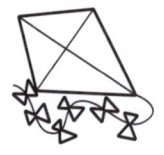   kite    eraser

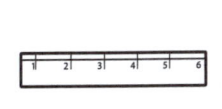

robot    pencil case    teddy bear   ruler 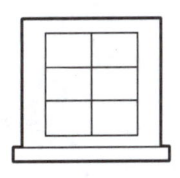   window

D5

UNIT 6 · MY DICTIONARY ·

Page 43 Find and circle the animals. Then write.

c_a_t   ___og   ra___ ___it   t___ ___tle   b___ ___d   h___ ___se

Page 47 Look and write.

sn___k___   sp___d___r   i___ ___a___a

m___ ___se   ___ ___og   ha___ ___ter

MY DICTIONARY

Page 52 Write words 1-6.

Page 56 Write words 7-12.

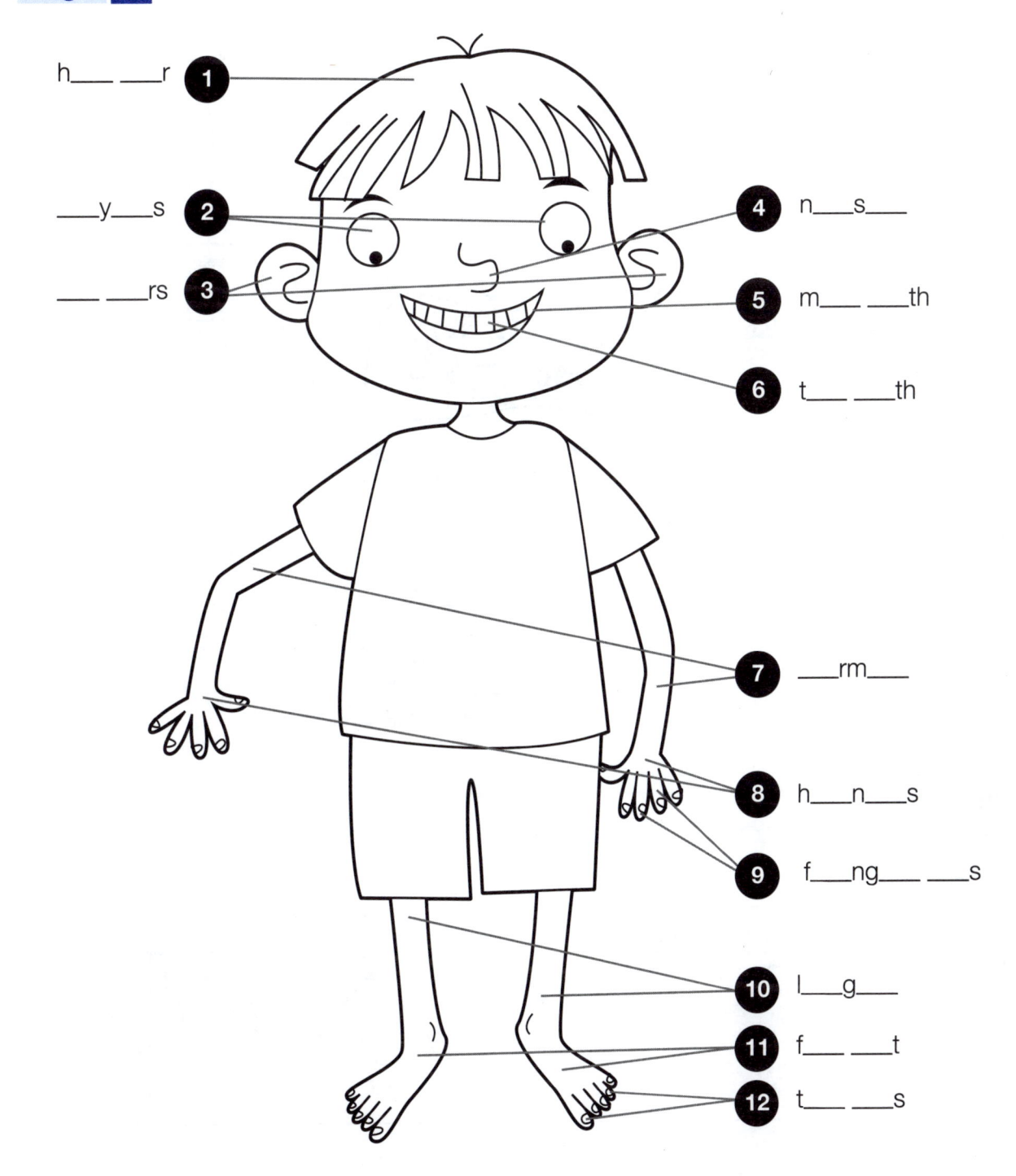

1. h___ ___r
2. ___y___s
3. ___ ___rs
4. n___s___
5. m___ ___th
6. t___ ___th
7. ___rm___
8. h___n___s
9. f___ng___ ___s
10. l___g___
11. f___ ___t
12. t___ ___s

UNIT 8 · MY DICTIONARY ·

Page 59 — Look and write.

pool park mall stadium school zoo

Page 63 — Write and draw.

tree
mountain
flower
river
beach
lake

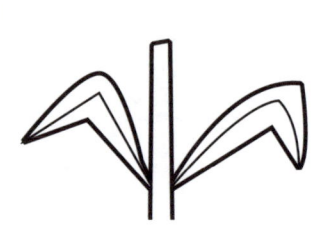

MY DICTIONARY

Page 68 Write and draw.

watermelon
banana
apple
pineapple
orange
pear

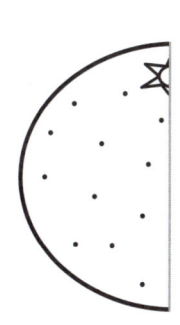

___ ___ ___ven — eight___ ___ ___ — f___ ___teen — four___ ___ ___ ___

Page 72 Write. Then complete the numbers.

11 18 15 14

19 18 12

nine___ ___ ___ ___ — th___ ___teen — t___ ___lve

20 17 16

twe___ ___ ___ — seven___ ___ ___ ___ — six___ ___ ___ ___

UNIT 10 · MY DICTIONARY ·

Page 75 Write and draw.

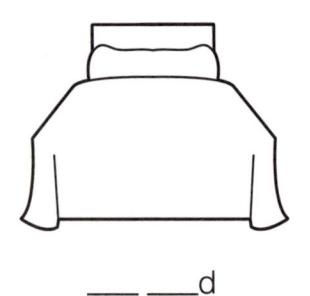

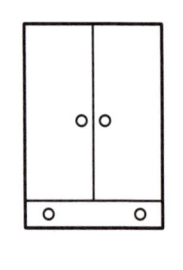

___ ___d

cl___s___t

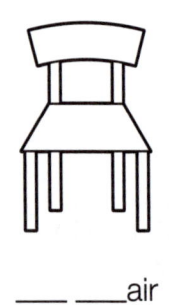

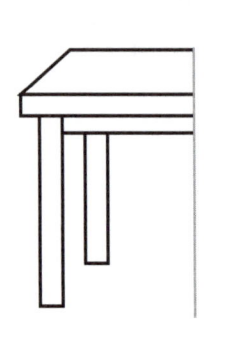

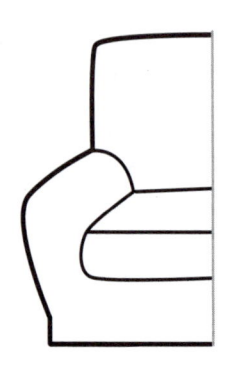

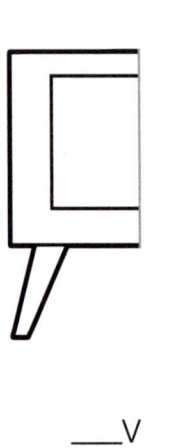

___ ___air

t___b___ ___

___ ___fa

___v

Page 79 Look and write.

living room
bedroom
bathroom
kitchen
garage
yard

NEXT STATION LEVEL 1 — PROGRESS RECORD

Read and circle.

1
Country: **UK** / **USA**
Hi. / **Goodbye**. My name's Eddie.

2
Country: **China** / **India**
Is it **a** / **an** elephant? **Yes**, / **No**, it is.

3
Country: **Russia** / **Brazil**
How old are you? I'm **seven**. / **fine**.

4
Country: **Japan** / **Spain**
Is he **a** / **an** farmer? **Yes**, / **No**, he isn't.

5
Country: **Egypt** / **Mexico**
Are they pink bikes? No, they **are**. / **aren't**.

6
Country: **Mexico** / **Egypt**
Do you have a frog? Yes, I **do**. / **don't**.

7
Country: **China** / **India**
Does **you** / **it** have eight legs? Yes, **you** / **it** does.

8
Country: **UK** / **USA**
There **is** / **isn't** a / **an** elephant in my school.

9
Country: **Brazil** / **Russia**
How many **orange** / **pears** are there? There are **one**. / **twelve**.

10
Country: **Spain** / **Japan**
Where's the **table**? / **chairs**? **It's** / **They're** in the kitchen.

Next Station ... Level 2!

2020 © Macmillan Education do Brasil

Based on *Next Move*
© Macmillan Publishers Limited 2013
Text © Cantabgilly Limited and Mary Charrington 2013
Adapted by Viv Lambert
Next Move is a registered trademark, property of Macmillan Publishers, 2013
First edition entitled "Next Stop" published 2009 by Macmillan Publishers

Director of Languages Brazil: Patrícia Souza De Luccia
Publishing Manager and Field Researcher: Patricia Muradas
Content Creation Coordinator: Cristina do Vale
Art Editor: Jean Aranha
Lead Editors: Ana Beatriz da Costa Moreira, Daniela Gonçala da Costa, Luciana Pereira da Silva
Content Editors: Millyane M. Moura Moreira, Tarsílio Soares Moreira
Digital Editor: Ana Paula Girardi
Editorial Assistant: Roberta Somera
Editorial Intern: Bruna Marques
Art Assistant: Denis Araujo
Art Intern: Jacqueline Alves
Graphic Production: Tatiane Romano, Thais Mendes P. Galvão
Proofreaders: Edward Willson, Márcia Leme, Sabrina Cairo Bileski
Design Concept: Design Divertido Artes Gráficas
Page Make-Up: Figurattiva Editorial
Image Processing: Jean Aranha, Jacqueline Alves, Denis Araujo
Audio: Argila Music, Núcleo de Criação
Cover Concept: Jean Aranha
Cover photography: CasarsaGuru/iStockphoto/Getty Images, Bubert/iStockphoto/Getty Images, LokFung/iStockphoto/Getty Images
Illustrations: Gustavo Gialuca (p. 6, 7, 13, 14, 22, 23, 29, 30, 38, 39, 45, 46, 54, 55, 61, 62, 70, 71, 77, 78, 84), Rita Gianetti | Sylvie Poggio (p. 11, 12, 21, 27, 32, 34, 36, 37, 41, 45, 50, 53, 57, 59, 66, 67, 76, 80, 95), David Harrington Studio Inc (p. 53), John Haslam (p. 63, 73, 79, D2, D3, D4, D5, D6, D7, D8, D9, D10, 95), Andrew Painter (p. 2, 3, 4, 5, 9, 10, 18, 19, 21, 25, 26, 33, 34, 35, 42, 49, 52, 56, 58, 60, 64, 65, 74, 81, 82, 95), Jim Peacock | Beehive Illustration (p. 8, 10, 15, 16, 17, 18, 26, 27, 28, 31, 33, 34, 40, 42, 43, 47, 49, 51, 58, 60, 65, 68, 69, 73, 75, 81), Tim Ruffle (p. 4-9, 11-16, 21, 24, 25, 27-32, 36, 37, 40, 41, 43, 44, 47, 48, 52, 53, 56, 57, 59, 60, 63, 64, 67-73, 75, 76, 80, 81, D1-D9).

Reproduction prohibited. Penal Code Article 184 and Law number 9.610 of February 19, 1998.

We would like to dedicate this book to teachers all over Brazil. We would also like to thank our clients and teachers who have helped us make this book better with their many rich contributions and feedback straight from the classroom!

Dados Internacionais de Catalogação na Publicação (CIP)
Bibliotecária responsável: Aline Graziele Benitez CRB-1/3129

C23n	Cant, Amanda
1.ed.	Next Station 1: Workbook / Amanda Cant; [Adapt.] Viv Lambert. – 1.ed. – São Paulo: Macmillan Education do Brasil, 2020.
	96 p.; il.; 21 x 27 cm. – (Coleção Next Station)
	ISBN: 978-85-511-0137-7
	1. Língua inglesa. I. Lambert, Viv. II. Título. III. Série. CDD 420

Índice para catálogo sistemático:
1. Língua inglesa

All rights reserved.

MACMILLAN EDUCATION DO BRASIL
Av. Brigadeiro Faria Lima, 1.309, 3º Andar –
Jd. Paulistano – São Paulo – SP – 01452-002
www.macmillan.com.br
Customer Service: [55] (11) 4613-2278
0800 16 88 77
Fax: [55] (11) 4612-6098

Printed in Brazil. First print. July, 2019.